Dan Evans, Steve Langfield and Alison Wright

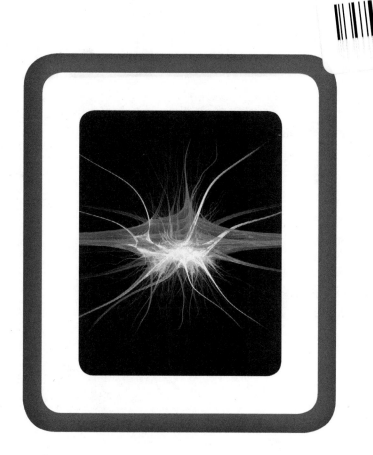

ESSENTIALS

Edexcel

INTERNATIONAL GCSE

Chemistry

Contents

Contents

States of Matter

Particle Theory

All matter exists as either a **solid**, **liquid** or **gas**. These are called the three states of matter.

The matter in each state is made up of very small **particles**, which are far too small to see. How these particles move and are arranged is known as **particle theory**.

Solids

In a **solid**, the particles are packed **very closely together** and each particle exerts a large pull force on every other particle around it.

Each particle has a small amount of energy so can only vibrate (move to and fro) about its fixed position, which doesn't change.

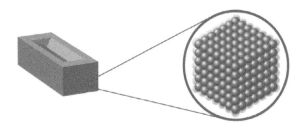

Liquids

In a **liquid**, the particles are packed **closely together** and each particle exerts a smaller pull force on every other particle around it.

The particles have enough energy to move around randomly, quickly and in any direction within the liquid.

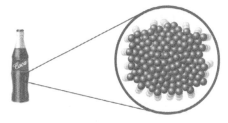

Gases

In a **gas**, the particles are **far apart** from each other and there is no pull force between the particles.

The particles have enough energy to move around quickly in any direction within their container.

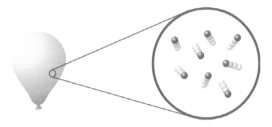

Changing State

A change of state occurs if a material changes from one state to another because energy is either given to it or taken away from it.

For example, look at the following example of ice, water and steam:

A small number of substances, when heated, change straight from a solid to a gas without becoming a liquid. This is called **sublimation**, e.g. iodine.

Melting

Ice melts into water at 0ºC.
Water freezes into ice at 0ºC.
This temperature is called the melting point.

Evaporating or boiling

Water boils into steam at 100ºC.
Steam condenses into water at 100ºC.
This temperature is called the boiling point.

Freezing or solidifying

Condensing

Key Words   Particle • Solid • Liquid • Gas • Sublimation

Using Particle Theory to Explain Change of State

The diagram below shows how the temperature of a material being heated would change against time.

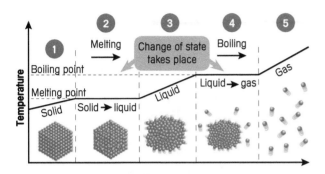

To begin with, the material is in its solid state.

1. As the solid is heated, the particles vibrate more and more.
2. The solid melts. The particles break away and begin to move around. This occurs at a fixed temperature called the melting point.
3. As the liquid is heated, the particles move around faster and faster.
4. The liquid boils. The particles begin to escape from the surface of the liquid. This occurs at a fixed temperature called the boiling point.
5. As the gas is heated, the particles move around even faster.

A change of state is an example of a physical change taking place, because it is possible to return to the material you started with. The change is reversible, i.e. if a gas is cooled down to a liquid and then to a solid, you could get a graph which is a mirror image of the one above:

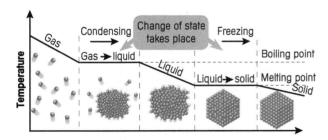

There are three important points to remember:

- When a change of state takes place, the **mass before** the change is **equal** to the **mass after** the change.

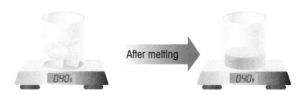

- Different substances would have graphs similar to those shown left, although they would change state at **different temperatures**.

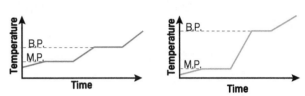

- The temperature stays constant when the state is changing.

Quick Test

1. Which state of matter has a fixed volume but a variable shape? *liquid*
2. In which state of matter do the particles possess the most kinetic energy? *gas*
3. Which two of the following changes of state are concerned with a liquid changing to a gas?
   Melting, Boiling, Sublimation, Freezing, Condensing, Evaporating
4. Which one of the following statements is incorrect?
   A: When a solid is heated, the particles vibrate more.
   B: When a liquid turns into a gas, there is a decrease in mass.
   C: Physical changes, such as melting, are reversible.

Atoms

Particles

Particles such as atoms and molecules are very small, much too small to see with the naked eye. When a coloured solid dissolves in water, the solution becomes coloured but the particles of the solid can't be seen. If the solution is diluted even more, the colour becomes fainter but the particles still can't be seen.

An example is when potassium manganate(VII) solution is diluted.

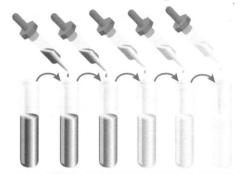

Successive Dilution of Potassium Manganate(VII) Solution

Diffusion

Particles in gases and liquids move about. **Diffusion** is when the particles of two or more different gases (or liquids) move about and mix together.

Diffusion in gases can be demonstrated by taking two jars of gas: one containing oxygen and the other bromine, a brownish gas. To begin with, the two gases are separated from each other. At the end, the concentrations of both bromine and oxygen are the same throughout the mixture.

The same effect can be seen using liquids. This takes longer because liquid particles move around more slowly compared to gas particles.

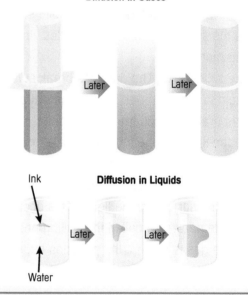

Diffusion in Gases

Later · Later

Ink

Diffusion in Liquids

Later · Later

Water

Elements and Atoms

All materials are made up of substances called **elements**. Most materials are made up of two or more different elements joined together. However, some materials are made up of only one kind of element. Elements are made up of atoms. Atoms are far too small for the eye to see. The atoms found in each element are unique to that element.

Mixtures and Compounds

A **mixture** is a substance made up of the atoms of two (or more) elements, or the molecules of two (or more) compounds, which have not been joined together in a chemical reaction. Mixtures are easy to separate and the composition of a mixture can vary.

In a **compound**, the atoms are chemically combined, e.g. iron and sulfur. The ratio of atoms in a compound is fixed.

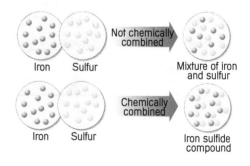

Iron · Sulfur · Not chemically combined · Mixture of iron and sulfur

Iron · Sulfur · Chemically combined · Iron sulfide compound

Separating Mixtures

The substances which make up a mixture can be separated from each other if necessary.

The following methods will normally be used.

Filtration is used to separate an insoluble solid from a liquid, e.g. a mixture of chalk and water.

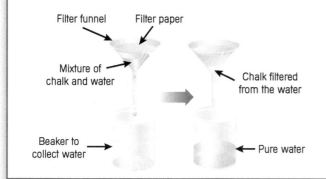

Filter funnel   Filter paper

Mixture of chalk and water

Chalk filtered from the water

Beaker to collect water

Pure water

Crystallisation is used to separate a soluble solid from a liquid when you want to collect the solid, e.g. a mixture of dissolved sugar and water. The slower the water is evaporated, the bigger the crystals.

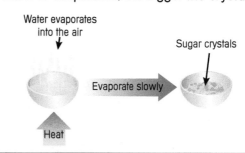

Water evaporates into the air

Sugar crystals

Evaporate slowly

Heat

Distillation is used to separate a liquid from any solids which are dissolved in it, in order to collect the liquid.

An example is producing pure water from sea water:

1. The salt water (sea water) is boiled and water turns to steam, which rises up the flask leaving the salt behind.
2. Steam (vapour) passes through the tubing and reaches the cold surface of the condenser where it condenses back to water.

Thermometer (measures temperature ot steam (vapour))

Slightly warmer water out

Condenser

Drops of water

Steam

Salt water solution

Cold water in (from tap)

Heat

Pure water

Fractional distillation is used to separate mixtures of liquids. It gives a better separation than simple distillation.

Fractional distillation can be used to separate a mixture of two liquids which have different boiling points.

For example, with a mixture of alcohol and water:

- the alcohol boils first (alcohol boils at about 78°C) and its vapour is condensed back into pure alcohol
- the water is left behind in the flask.

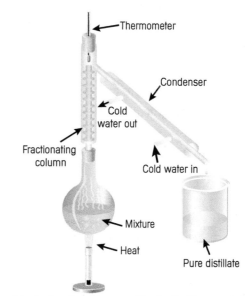

Thermometer

Condenser

Cold water out

Fractionating column

Cold water in

Mixture

Heat

Pure distillate

The fractionating column enables the liquid vapour to boil and condense a number of times before it reaches the top and travels into the condenser. This improves the separation of the liquids.

Atoms

Paper Chromatography

Paper chromatography is used to separate small amounts of two or more solids that are soluble in a particular liquid (solvent). For example, it can be used to separate the different solids, called pigments, in a particular colour of ink.

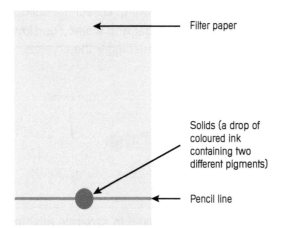

Filter paper

Solids (a drop of coloured ink containing two different pigments)

Pencil line

1. If the mixture of pigments (solids) has not already been dissolved in water (the solvent), a solution needs to be made up.
2. A concentrated drop of the solution is put on the filter paper on the pencil line. The water in the solution evaporates to leave the pigments behind.
3. This can be repeated to produce a more concentrated spot.
4. The pigment being investigated must remain just above the water level which covers the bottom 1cm of the filter paper.
5. As the water rises up the paper, the pigments dissolve in the water and are carried up the paper. The more soluble pigments travel further up the paper.
6. This is a chromatogram.

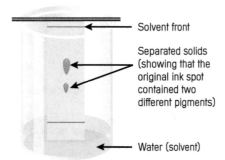

Solvent front

Separated solids (showing that the original ink spot contained two different pigments)

Water (solvent)

Here is a chromatogram of the pigments contained in an unknown ink, X, and four other inks.

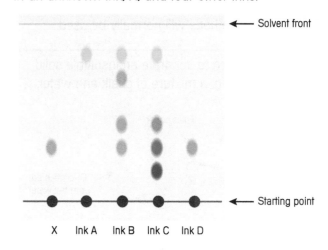

Solvent front

Starting point

X   Ink A   Ink B   Ink C   Ink D

By comparing the chromatograms, you can see that the unknown ink 'X' is ink 'D'.

This method of identifying substances using known chromatograms has many uses, especially by the police in forensic science.

Quick Test

1. When a crystal of purple potassium permanganate is added to a beaker of water, the water slowly turns purple. What name is given to this process?
2. Which one of the following statements about compounds is incorrect?
   A: Compounds contain elements in constant proportions.
   B: Compounds contain more than one element chemically bonded together.
   C: The elements in a compound are easy to separate.
3. Which method of separation is most suitable for separating a mixture of liquids?
4. Copper(II) sulfate is soluble in water. Which method of separation is most suitable for obtaining crystals of copper(II) sulfate?

Atoms

An **atom** has a **small central nucleus**, made up of **protons** and **neutrons**. The nucleus is surrounded by **electrons**, which are arranged in orbits called **shells**.

An atom has the same number of protons as electrons, so the atom as a whole is **neutral** (i.e. it has no electrical charge).

A proton has the same **mass** as a neutron. The mass of an electron is **negligible** (nearly zero).

All atoms of the same element have the same number of protons.

Atomic Particle	Relative Mass	Relative Charge
Proton	1	+1
Neutron	1	0
Electron	Nearly zero	−1

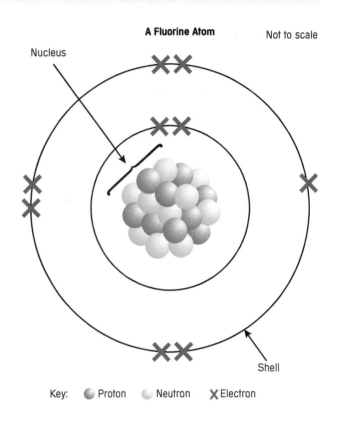

A Fluorine Atom   Not to scale

Nucleus

Shell

Key: ● Proton   ○ Neutron   ✗ Electron

Atomic Number and Mass Number

The **atomic number** (proton number) is the number of **protons** in an atom.

The **mass number** is the total number of **protons** and **neutrons** in an atom.

The elements in the Periodic Table are arranged in **increasing atomic number**.

Element	Protons	Electrons	Neutrons
Hydrogen atom $^{1}_{1}H$	1	1	0 $1 - 1 = 0$
Helium atom $^{4}_{2}He$	2	2	2 $4 - 2 = 2$
Sodium atom $^{23}_{11}Na$	11	11	12 $23 - 11 = 12$

You can use information from the Periodic Table to work out the number of protons, electrons and neutrons in any atom.

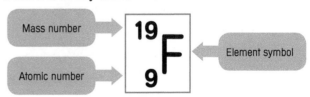

Mass number

Atomic number

Element symbol

$^{19}_{9}F$

For example, consider $^{19}_{9}F$. The atomic number is the number of protons. In this instance, fluorine has nine protons. For the atom to be neutral, it must have the same number of electrons: nine. The mass number of the atom is 19, and only protons and neutrons have mass, so the rest of the mass (19 minus 9) must come from neutrons. So fluorine atoms have 10 neutrons.

Atomic Structure

Isotopes

Isotopes are **atoms** of the **same element** that have the **same atomic number** but a **different mass number**, i.e. a different number of neutrons.

For example, chlorine has two isotopes:

$$^{35}_{17}\text{Cl} \quad \text{Mass number } = 35 \quad \text{Atomic number} = 17$$

$$^{37}_{17}\text{Cl} \quad \text{Mass number } = 37 \quad \text{Atomic number} = 17$$

You can identify isotopes from data about the number of electrons, protons and neutrons in particles. Each isotope has the **same number of protons** and **electrons**, but a **different number** of **neutrons**. For example, carbon has three main isotopes, as listed in this table.

Isotope	Symbol	Mass number	Atomic number	Protons	Neutrons	Electrons
Carbon-12	$^{12}_{6}\text{C}$	12	6	6	6	6
Carbon-13	$^{13}_{6}\text{C}$	13	6	6	7	6
Carbon-14	$^{14}_{6}\text{C}$	14	6	6	8	6

Relative Atomic Mass, A_r

Every element has its own **relative atomic mass**, A_r.

Each element in the Periodic Table has two numbers. The **larger** of the two numbers is the A_r. For example, the A_r of carbon is 12.

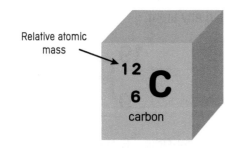

Relative atomic mass

$$^{12}_{6}\text{C}$$
carbon

The A_r is the mass of a particular atom compared with a twelfth of the mass of a carbon atom (the C-12 isotope).

By looking at the Periodic Table, you can see that:
- carbon is 12 times heavier than hydrogen, but is only half as heavy as magnesium
- magnesium is three-quarters as heavy as sulfur
- sulfur is twice as heavy as oxygen, etc.

The A_r is an **average** value for all the **isotopes** of the element.

The A_r of an element can be calculated from the **relative abundance** of a normal sample of the element and the mass numbers of the different isotopes it contains.

> **Example**
>
> The relative abundance of a sample of chlorine is 75% of the isotope ^{35}Cl and 25% of the isotope ^{37}Cl. Calculate the A_r.
>
> Work out the mass of each isotope by multiplying the percentage by the mass number, e.g. 75% × 35 and 25% × 37.
>
> Add all the masses together to get the total mass and then divide by 100 to get the average.
>
> The relative atomic mass of chlorine
> $$= \frac{(75 \times 35) + (25 \times 37)}{100} = \textbf{35.5}$$

Electron Configuration

The **electron configuration** of an atom shows how the electrons are arranged in shells around the nucleus:

- The electrons in an atom fill up the lowest energy level first. This is the shell closest to the nucleus.
- The first shell can hold up to two electrons.
- The shells after this can hold up to eight electrons.

An electron configuration is written as a series of numbers, e.g. 2.8.1. Going across a **period**, electron configurations increase by one, e.g. sodium 2.8.1, magnesium 2.8.2, aluminium 2.8.3, until the outer shell is full, e.g. argon 2.8.8.

N.B. This is only true for the first 20 elements.

The number of electrons in the outer shell of an atom is important as it helps explain how an atom bonds to other atoms. There is a quick way to work out the number of electrons in the outer shell of an atom — it is the same as the group number of the element in the Periodic Table.

For example:

- carbon is in Group 4 — it has 4 electrons in its outer shell.
- magnesium is in Group 2 — it has 2 electrons in its outer shell.

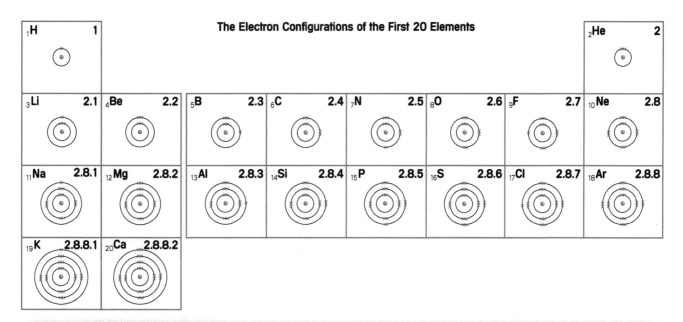

The Electron Configurations of the First 20 Elements

Quick Test

1. The number of protons in an atom is equal to the number of ....
2. What is meant by the mass number of an atom?
3. What are the numbers of protons, neutrons and electrons in the following atom?

$$^{23}_{11}\text{Na}$$

4. What are isotopes? *are atoms of the same element that have the same atomic number but different mass number*
5. What is the relative atomic mass of an atom? *average value for all isotopes in an element*

Relative Formula Masses

Relative Formula Mass, M_r

The **relative formula mass**, M_r, of a compound is the sum of the relative atomic masses of all the atoms present in the formula.

Follow these steps to calculate the M_r:

1. Write down the formula of the compound.
2. Multiply the number of atoms of each element in the formula by its A_r.
3. Add them all up.

H	S	O	Ca
$A_r = 1$	$A_r = 32$	$A_r = 16$	$A_r = 40$

Example

Calculate the relative formula mass of H_2SO_4.

Write the symbols. Multiply the number of atoms in the formula by the A_r.

H	2×1	$= 2$
S	1×32	$= 32$
O	4×16	$= 64$

Add them all up.

$$M_r = 98$$

The Mole

A **mole** (mol) is a measure of the **number of particles** (atoms, molecules, ions or electrons) contained in a substance. One mole of a substance is its relative formula mass or its relative atomic mass in grams.

P2 One mole of **any substance** (element or compound) will always contain the **same number** of particles – six hundred thousand billion billion, or 6×10^{23}. This is called the Avogadro number.

If a substance is an **element**, the mass of one mole of the substance, called the molar mass (g/mol), is always **equal** to the **relative atomic mass** of the substance in grams. For example, the molar mass of hydrogen is 1g/mol, of oxygen is 16g/mol and of sodium is 23g/mol.

If a substance is a **compound**, the mass of one mole of the substance is always **equal** to the **relative formula mass** of the substance in grams. For example, the mass of one mole of sodium hydroxide (NaOH) is 40g (the M_r of NaOH is 40).

You can calculate the number of moles in a substance using this formula:

$$\text{Number of moles of substance (mol)} = \frac{\text{Mass of substance (g)}}{\text{Mass of one mole (g/mol)}}$$

N.B. You need to remember this equation as it will not be given to you in the exam.

Example 1

Calculate the number of moles of carbon dioxide (CO_2) in 33g of the gas.

$$\text{Number of moles of substance} = \frac{\text{Mass of substance}}{\text{Mass of one mole}}$$

M_r carbon dioxide = A_r carbon + $(2 \times A_r$ oxygen)
= $12 + (2 \times 16)$
= 44

$$= \frac{33g}{44g/mol} = \textbf{0.75 mole}$$

Example 2

Calculate the mass of four moles of sodium hydroxide.

$$\text{Mass of substance} = \text{Number of moles of substance} \times \text{Mass of one mole}$$

$$= 4mol \times 40g/mol = \textbf{160g}$$

Quick Test

1. Calculate the relative formula mass of the following compounds.
   a) Li_2O (A_r for Li = 7 and A_r for O = 16)
   b) $(NH_4)_2SO_4$ (A_r for N = 14, A_r for H = 1, A_r for S = 32 and A_r for O = 16)

Measuring Gas Volumes

It is difficult to weigh a gas to determine the amount of gas in a reaction (i.e. how many moles of gas). It is more convenient to measure the volume of a gas.

Apparatus for Collecting and Measuring Volume of Gas made in a Reaction

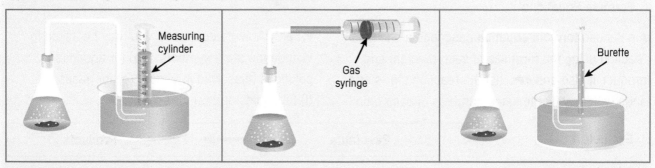

 ## Calculating Volumes and Amounts of Gases

One mole of any gas occupies a volume of **24dm^3** at room temperature and pressure (rtp). This is known as the **molar volume**. Remember, we often measure volumes in cm^3. The molar volume in cm^3 is 24 000cm^3 because 1dm^3 = 1000cm^3.

You can use this rule to:
- calculate the volume of a known amount of gas
- calculate the amount of gas if the volume is known.

Volume (in dm^3) = Moles of gas × 24 OR **Volume (in cm^3) = Moles of gas × 24 000**
Moles = $\dfrac{\text{Volume (in dm}^3)}{24}$ OR   **Moles = $\dfrac{\text{Volume (in cm}^3)}{24\ 000}$**

Example 1

What is the volume of half a mole of nitrogen at rtp?

Volume (dm^3) = 0.5 × 24 = **12dm^3**

Example 2

A balloon is filled with oxygen until it has a volume of 6dm^3 at rtp. How many moles of oxygen are in the balloon?

$$\text{Moles} = \frac{6}{24} = \textbf{0.25 mole}$$

Example 3

Calculate the volume (in cm^3) of carbon dioxide when 0.045 moles of it are made in a reaction at rtp.

$$\text{Volume} = 0.045 × 24\ 000 = \textbf{1080cm}^3$$

Example 4

A student burned 480cm^3 of methane in an experiment. Calculate how many moles of gas she used at rtp.

$$\text{Moles} = \frac{480}{24\ 000} = \textbf{0.02 mole}$$

Quick Test

1. What is the volume of 2 moles of carbon dioxide gas at rtp?
2. How many moles are present in 3dm^3 of methane gas at rtp?

Chemical Formulae and Chemical Equations

Writing Balanced Equations

Word equations describe a chemical reaction using the names of the reactants and products. Do not include any formulae in a word equation.

For example:

Reactants ➔ Products

methane + oxygen ➔ carbon dioxide + water

Formula Equations

A balanced **formula equation** describes a chemical reaction using the formulae of each reactant and product. It also ensures that the reaction starts and ends with exactly the same numbers of each atom.

When you write equations, you may be asked to include the **state symbols**: (aq) for aqueous solutions (dissolved in water), (g) for gases, (l) for liquids and (s) for solids.

Example 1

1. Write a word equation.
2. Substitute in symbols and formulae.
3. Balance the equation.
   - First, you need to add another MgO to the product side to balance the O atoms.
   - You now need to add another Mg on the reactant side to balance the Mg atoms.
   - There are two magnesium atoms and two oxygen atoms on each side – it's balanced.
4. Write a balanced symbol equation.

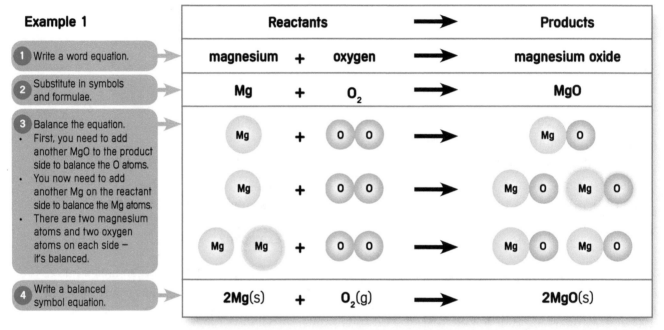

	Reactants	➔	Products
	magnesium + oxygen	➔	magnesium oxide
	Mg + O_2	➔	MgO
	$2Mg(s)$ + $O_2(g)$	➔	$2MgO(s)$

You should be able to balance equations by looking at the formulae (i.e. without drawing the atoms).

Example 2

1. Write a word equation.
2. Substitute in symbols and formulae.
3. Balance the equation.
4. Write a balanced symbol equation with state symbols.

calcium carbonate + nitric acid ➔	calcium nitrate + carbon dioxide + water
$CaCO_3$ + HNO_3 ➔	$Ca(NO_3)_2$ + CO_2 + H_2O
$CaCO_3$ + $2HNO_3$ ➔	$Ca(NO_3)_2$ + CO_2 + H_2O
$CaCO_3(s)$ + $2HNO_3(aq)$ ➔	$Ca(NO_3)_2(aq)$ + $CO_2(g)$ + $H_2O(l)$

Equations can also be written using displayed formulae. These must be balanced too.

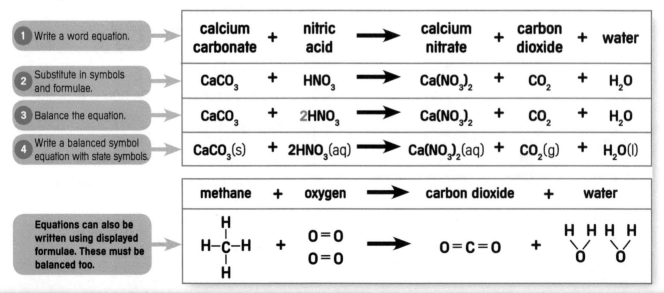

Chemical Formulae and Chemical Equations

Mass of Elements in a Compound

The **mass** of a compound is made up of the masses of all its elements added together. So, if you know the mass of a compound and the mass of one of the elements, you can calculate the mass of the other element.

Example

80g of copper(II) oxide contains 16g of oxygen. What mass of copper does it contain?

Mass of copper + 16g = 80g

Mass of copper = 80g − 16g = **64g**

Empirical Formula

The **empirical formula** is the simplest whole number ratio of each type of atom in a compound. For example, hexene (C_6H_{12}) has the empirical formula C_1H_2, or CH_2.

You can work out the empirical formula of a substance from its chemical formula. For example, the empirical formula of ethanoic acid (CH_3COOH) is CH_2O.

The empirical formula of a compound can be calculated from **either**:

* the percentage composition of the compound by mass **or**
* the mass of each element in the compound.

To calculate the empirical formula, do the following:
1. List all the elements in the compound.
2. Divide the data for each element by its A_r (to find out the number of moles).
3. Select the smallest answer from Step 2 and divide each answer by that result to obtain a ratio.
4. The ratio may have to be scaled up to give whole numbers.

Example 1

What is the empirical formula of a hydrocarbon containing 75% carbon? (Hydrogen = 25%)

1. Carbon : Hydrogen
2. $\frac{75}{12}$: $\frac{25}{1}$
3. ÷6.25 6.25 : 25 ÷6.25
4. 1 : 4

So the empirical formula is C_1H_4, or **CH_4**.

Example 2

What is the empirical formula of a compound containing 24g of carbon, 8g of hydrogen and 32g of oxygen?

1. Carbon : Hydrogen : Oxygen
2. $\frac{24}{12}$: $\frac{8}{1}$: $\frac{32}{16}$
3. 2 : 8 : 2
    ÷2   ÷2   ÷2
4. 1 : 4 : 1

So the empirical formula is **CH_4O**.

Quick Test

1. Balance the following equation:
   $Al + O_2 \longrightarrow Al_2O_3$
2. 3g of carbon dioxide contains 0.82g of carbon. What mass of oxygen is present in this sample?
3. Calculate the empirical formula of the following:
   a) A compound containing 0.35g of lithium and 0.40g of oxygen (A_r for Li = 7 and A_r for O = 16)
   b) A sample of iron oxide containing 70% iron (A_r for Fe = 56 and A_r for O = 16)

Key Words Empirical formula

Chemical Formulae and Chemical Equations

Molecular Formula

The **molecular formula** is the **actual** whole number ratio of each type of atom in a compound. It can be the same as the empirical formula or a multiple of the empirical formula. To convert an empirical formula into a molecular formula, you also need to know the relative formula mass of the compound (M_r).

Example

A compound has an empirical formula of CH_2 and a M_r of 42. What is its molecular formula? (A_r for C = 12 and A_r for H = 1)

Work out the relative formula mass of the empirical formula = $12 + (2 \times 1) = 14$

Then divide the actual M_r by the empirical formula $M_r = \dfrac{42}{14} = 3$. This gives the multiple.

The molecular formula is $3 \times CH_2 = \mathbf{C_3H_6}$

Determining a Formula by Experiment

Metal Oxides

The formula of a **metal oxide** such as magnesium oxide can be determined by heating a known amount of magnesium in air. The amount of oxygen that reacts with the magnesium can be calculated by weighing the magnesium before and after the reaction.

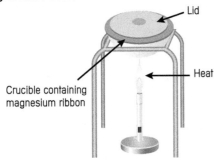

Lid

Heat

Crucible containing magnesium ribbon

An alternative method would be to start with a known amount of a metal oxide and remove the oxygen. This method is suitable for an oxide of a less reactive metal, such as copper.

The oxide is heated in a stream of a suitable gas, such as hydrogen or some domestic gas supplies. The amounts of metal and oxygen can be calculated by weighing them before and after the reaction.

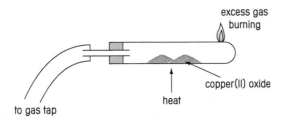

excess gas burning

copper(II) oxide

to gas tap

heat

Example

1.50g of magnesium was heated in air until it had all reacted. 2.50g of magnesium oxide was formed. What is the formula of magnesium oxide? (A_r for Mg = 24 and A_r for O = 16)

Mass of oxygen reacted with the magnesium = $2.50 - 1.50 = 1.00$g

Moles of O reacted = $\dfrac{1.00}{16} = 0.0625$ moles

Moles of Mg reacted = $\dfrac{1.50}{24} = 0.0625$ moles

Ratio of 0.0625 magnesium : 0.0625 oxygen = 1 : 1

Formula = **MgO**

Example

1.98g of copper(II) oxide was heated in a gas stream until it had all reacted. 1.58g of copper was formed. What is the formula of copper(II) oxide? (A_r for Cu = 63.5 and A_r for O = 16)

Mass of oxygen reacted with the copper = $1.98 - 1.58 = 0.40$g

Moles of O reacted = $\dfrac{0.40}{16} = 0.025$ moles

Moles of Cu reacted = $\dfrac{1.58}{63.5} = 0.025$ moles

Ratio of 0.025 copper : 0.025 oxygen = 1 : 1

Formula = **CuO**

Determining a Formula by Experiment (Cont.)

Water

The formula of **water** can be determined by decomposing it into hydrogen and oxygen in a process called electrolysis (see page 26). The volume of each gas made can be used to calculate how many moles of each gas are made. This is then converted into the formula.

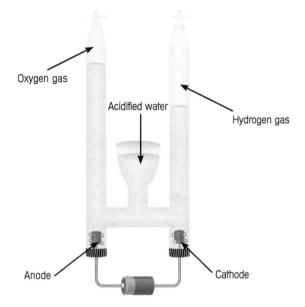

As you can see from the diagram, twice as much hydrogen is produced than oxygen, i.e. 2 volumes of hydrogen to 1 volume of oxygen.

The same volume of any gas contains the same number of moles. So the mole ratio for water is:
2 moles of hydrogen to 1 mole of oxygen $\rightarrow$ H_2O

Water of Crystallisation

The crystals of some salts contain water as part of the crystal structure. This is called **water of crystallisation**.

For example, sodium carbonate (Na_2CO_3) crystals have 10 molecules of water for each sodium carbonate unit in the crystal structure, and so the formula is written $Na_2CO_3 \cdot 10H_2O$.

To determine the number of water molecules in a crystal structure, do the following:

1. Weigh a sample of the crystals.
2. Heat the crystals gently to break down the crystals and evaporate the water until there is no further change in mass.
3. Weigh the remaining substance and use it to calculate the amount of water removed.

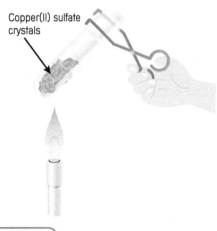

Copper(II) sulfate crystals

Example

4.99g of hydrated copper(II) sulfate was heated gently until all the water had been removed from the crystals. 3.19g of anhydrous copper(II) sulfate was formed. What is the formula of the hydrated crystals? (M_r $CuSO_4$ = 159.5 and M_r H_2O = 18)

Mass of water removed from crystals
$$= 4.99 - 3.19 = 1.80g$$

Moles of water removed $= \dfrac{1.80}{18} = 0.10$ moles

$$\dfrac{\text{Moles of copper(II)}}{\text{sulfate remaining}} = \dfrac{3.19}{159.5}$$

$$= 0.02 \text{ moles}$$

Ratio of 0.02 moles copper(II) sulfate : 0.10 moles water

$$= 1 \text{ mole copper(II) sulfate to } \dfrac{0.10}{0.02}$$

$$= 5 \text{ moles water}$$

Formula = **$CuSO_4 \cdot 5H_2O$**

Chemical Formulae and Chemical Equations

Calculations using Equations and Masses

Calculating the Mass of a Product

> **Example**
>
> Calculate how much calcium oxide can be produced from 50kg of calcium carbonate.
> (A_r for Ca = 40, A_r for C = 12 and A_r for O = 16)
>
> **1** Write down the equation.
>
> $$CaCO_3 \longrightarrow CaO + CO_2$$
>
> **2** Work out the M_r of each substance and multiply by the number of moles of that substance from the equation.
>
> $$40 + 12 + (3 \times 16) \longrightarrow (40 + 16) + [12 + (2 \times 16)]$$
>
> **3** Check that the total mass of reactants equals the total mass of the products. If they are not the same, check your work.
>
> $$100 \longrightarrow 56 + 44 ✔$$
>
> **4** The question only mentions calcium oxide and calcium carbonate, so you can now ignore the carbon dioxide. You just need the ratio of mass of reactant to mass of product.
>
> $$100 : 56$$
>
> **5** Use the ratio to calculate how much calcium oxide can be produced.

If 100kg of $CaCO_3$ produces 56kg of CaO, then 1kg of $CaCO_3$ produces $\dfrac{56}{100}$ kg of CaO, and 50kg of $CaCO_3$ produces $\dfrac{56}{100} \times 50$ = **28kg of CaO**

Calculating the Mass of a Reactant

> **Example**
>
> Calculate how much aluminium oxide is needed to produce 540 tonnes of aluminium.
> (A_r for Al = 27 and A_r for O = 16)
>
> **1** Write down the equation.
>
> $$2Al_2O_3 \longrightarrow 4Al + 3O_2$$
>
> **2** Work out the M_r of each substance and multiply by the number of moles of that substance from the equation.
>
> $$2 \times [(2 \times 27) + (3 \times 16)] \longrightarrow (4 \times 27) + [3 \times (2 \times 16)]$$
>
> **3** Check that the total mass of reactants equals the total mass of the products. If they are not the same, check your work.
>
> $$204 \longrightarrow 108 + 96 ✔$$
>
> **4** The question only mentions aluminium oxide and aluminium, so you can now ignore the oxygen. You just need the ratio of mass of reactant to mass of product.
>
> $$204 : 108$$
>
> **5** Use the ratio to calculate how much aluminium oxide is needed.

If 204 tonnes of Al_2O_3 produces 108 tonnes of Al, then $\dfrac{204}{108}$ tonnes is needed to produce 1 tonne of Al, and $\dfrac{204}{108} \times 540$ is needed to produce 540 tonnes of Al = **1020 tonnes of Al_2O_3**

Quick Test

1 An oxide of phosphorus has an empirical formula of P_2O_5 and a M_r of 284. What is its molecular formula? (A_r for P = 31 and A_r for O = 16)

2 A 1.6g sample of copper was heated in oxygen. At the end of the experiment, the mass of copper oxide formed was 2.0g. What is the formula of the copper oxide formed? (A_r for Cu = 63.5 and A_r for O = 16)

3 2.50g of lead oxide was heated in a stream of hydrogen. At the end of the experiment, the lead remaining had a mass of 2.32g. What is the formula of the lead oxide? (A_r for Pb = 208 and A_r for O = 16)

4 What mass of sulfur dioxide is formed when 2.1g of sulfur reacts with oxygen?
(A_r for S = 32 and A_r for O = 16) $S + O_2 \longrightarrow SO_2$

Chemical Formulae and Chemical Equations

 P2 Percentage Yield

Percentage yield is a way of comparing the amount of product made (**actual yield**) to the amount of product expected to be made (**predicted yield**).

You can calculate percentage yield by using this formula:

$$\text{Percentage yield} = \frac{\text{Actual yield}}{\text{Predicted yield}} \times 100$$

- A **100% yield** means that **no product has been lost** (actual yield is the same as predicted yield).
- A **0% yield** means that **no product has been made** (actual yield is zero).

Example

A reaction was expected to produce a mass of 10g. The actual mass produced was 8g. Calculate the percentage yield.

$$\text{Percentage yield} = \frac{\text{Actual yield}}{\text{Predicted yield}} \times 100$$

$$= \frac{8g}{10g} \times 100 = \textbf{80\%}$$

There are several reasons why the percentage yield is less than the expected yield. The products could be lost in **evaporation, filtration** or during the **transfer of liquids**. Not all reactants may have been used to make the products. The reactants may have been impure.

Concentration

The concentration of a solution depends on the amount of solute (in moles) that is dissolved in a volume of solution (measured in dm^3). Volumes are often measured in cm^3. It is very important to convert them into dm^3 before calculating the concentration.

To convert a volume:
- from cm^3 into dm^3, divide it by 1000
- from dm^3 into cm^3, multiply it by 1000.

The concentration of a solution can be calculated using this formula:

$$\frac{\text{Concentration of solution}}{(\text{mol/dm}^3 \text{ or M})} = \frac{\text{Number of moles of solute (mole)}}{\text{Volume of solution (dm}^3)}$$

Example 1

Calculate the concentration in mol/dm^3 of a solution that contains 0.24 moles of sodium hydroxide dissolved in $2dm^3$ of solution.

$$\frac{\text{Concentration}}{\text{of solution}} = \frac{\text{Number of moles of solute}}{\text{Volume of solution}}$$

$$= \frac{0.24}{2} = \textbf{0.12mol/dm}^3$$

Example 2

Calculate the concentration in mol/dm^3 of $200cm^3$ of a solution that contains 5.85g of sodium chloride. (M_r NaCl = 58.5)

$$\text{Convert the volume to dm}^3 = \frac{200}{1000} = 0.2dm^3$$

Calculate the number of moles of NaCl

$$= \frac{\text{Mass}}{\text{Molar mass}} = \frac{5.85}{58.5} = 0.1 \text{ mole}$$

$$\frac{\text{Concentration}}{\text{of solution}} = \frac{\text{Number of moles of solute}}{\text{Volume of solution}}$$

$$= \frac{0.1}{0.2} = \textbf{0.5mol/dm}^3$$

N.B. mol/dm^3 is the same as $mol\ dm^{-3}$

Quick Test

1. In an experiment the expected amount of product was 16.30g. However, only 12.60g of product was actually produced. What is the percentage yield for this experiment?
2. Calculate the concentration (in mol/dm^3) of $200cm^3$ of a solution containing 9.1g of potassium nitrate (KNO_3). (A_r of K = 39, A_r of N = 14 and A_r of O = 16)

Ionic Compounds

Ions

An **ion** is **an atom** (or group of atoms) that has lost or gained electrons, e.g. Na^+, Cl^-, NH_4^+, SO_4^{2-}.

A **positive ion** is made when an atom, or group of atoms, **loses** one or more **electrons**. For example, losing two electrons makes a 2^+ ion, e.g. Mg^{2+}.

Atom or group of atoms — Electron(s) ⟶ Positive ion

A **negative ion** is made when an atom, or group of atoms, **gains** one or more **electrons**. For example, gaining two electrons makes a 2^- ion, e.g. O^{2-}.

Atom or group of atoms **+** Electron(s) ⟶ Negative ion

By looking at an equation of the formation of an ion, you can decide whether it is **oxidation** or **reduction**:

- If **electrons** are **added**, it's a **reduction** reaction.
- If **electrons** are **taken away**, it's an **oxidation** reaction.

An easy way to remember the definitions of oxidation and reduction is by thinking of **OILRIG**:

- **O**xidation **I**s **L**oss of electrons.
- **R**eduction **I**s **G**ain of electrons.

The Ionic Bond

When a metal and a non-metal combine, electrons are transferred from one **atom** to the other, forming **ions**. Each ion will have a complete outer shell.

In **ionic bonding**:

- the metal atom loses all outer-shell **electrons** to become a **positive ion**
- the non-metal atom **gains electrons** to fill its outer shell and become a **negative ion**
- the positive and negative ions are attracted to each other – this attraction is an **ionic bond**.

Becoming a positive ion

- An atom with 1 outer-shell electron (Group 1) will form a 1^+ ion, e.g. Li^+, Na^+, K^+, H^+.
- Atoms with 2 outer-shell electrons (Group 2) will form a 2^+ ion, e.g. Mg^{2+}, Ca^{2+}.
- Atoms with 3 outer-shell electrons (Group 3) will form a 3^+ ion, e.g. Al^{3+}.

Becoming a negative ion

- An atom with 7 electrons in its outer electron shell (Group 7) will form a 1^- ion, e.g. Cl^-, Br^-, I^-
- Atoms with 6 electrons in their outer electron shell (Group 6) will form a 2^- ion, e.g. O^{2-}
- Atoms with 5 electrons in their outer electron shell (Group 5) will form a 3^- ion, e.g. N^{3-}

Example 1: Sodium chloride

sodium + chlorine ⟶ sodium chloride

$$2Na(s) + Cl_2(g) \longrightarrow 2NaCl(s)$$

1. The sodium atom has 1 electron in its outer shell.
2. The electron is transferred to the chlorine atom. Both atoms now have 8 electrons in their outer shell (a stable octet).
3. The atoms become ions (Na^+ and Cl^-).
4. The compound formed is sodium chloride, NaCl.

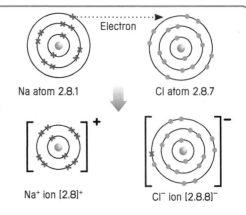

Electron

Na atom 2.8.1   Cl atom 2.8.7

Na^+ ion $[2.8]^+$ Cl^- ion $[2.8.8]^-$

The Ionic Bond (Cont.)

Example 2: Magnesium oxide

magnesium + oxygen ➡ magnesium oxide

$2Mg(s) + O_2(g) \rightarrow 2MgO(s)$

1 The magnesium atom has 2 electrons in its outer shell.
2 The 2 electrons are transferred to the oxygen atom. Both atoms now have 8 electrons in their outer shell.
3 The atoms become ions (Mg^{2+} and O^{2-}).
4 The compound formed is magnesium oxide, MgO.

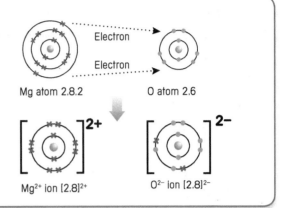

Mg atom 2.8.2   O atom 2.6

Mg^{2+} ion $[2.8]^{2+}$ O^{2-} ion $[2.8]^{2-}$

Example 3: Sodium oxide

sodium + oxygen ➡ sodium oxide

$4Na(s) + O_2(g) \rightarrow 2Na_2O(s)$

1 The sodium atom has 1 electron in its outer shell.
2 An oxygen atom needs 2 electrons, so 2 sodium atoms are needed.
3 The atoms become ions (Na^+, Na^+ and O^{2-}).
4 The compound formed is sodium oxide, Na_2O.

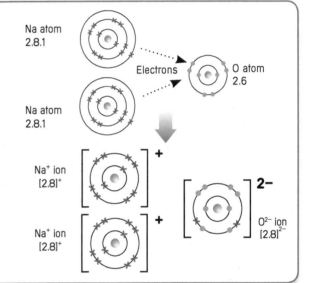

Na atom 2.8.1   Na atom 2.8.1   Electrons   O atom 2.6

Na^+ ion $[2.8]^+$ Na^+ ion $[2.8]^+$ O^{2-} ion $[2.8]^{2-}$

Example 4: Magnesium chloride

magnesium + chlorine ➡ magnesium chloride

$Mg(s) + Cl_2(g) \rightarrow MgCl_2(s)$

1 The magnesium atom has 2 electrons in its outer shell.
2 A chlorine atom only needs 1 electron, so 2 chlorine atoms are needed.
3 The atoms become ions (Mg^{2+}, Cl^- and Cl^-).
4 The compound formed is magnesium chloride, $MgCl_2$.

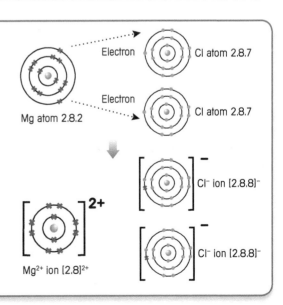

Mg atom 2.8.2   Cl atom 2.8.7   Cl atom 2.8.7

Mg^{2+} ion $[2.8]^{2+}$ Cl^- ion $[2.8.8]^-$ Cl^- ion $[2.8.8]^-$

Ionic Compounds

The Structure of Ionic Compounds

Ionic compounds are giant structures of ions. They are held together by **strong forces** of attraction (electrostatic forces) between **oppositely charged ions**. The forces act in **all directions**. This type of bonding is called **ionic bonding**.

Ionic compounds:

- **conduct electricity** when molten or in solution because the charged ions are free to move about and a current flows when the charged particles move.
- have **high melting** and **boiling points** because of the strong electrostatic forces between the oppositely charged ions.

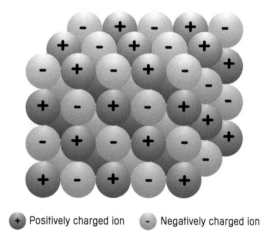

 Positively charged ion   Negatively charged ion

P2 Ionic Crystals

Ionic compounds such as sodium chloride form a three-dimensional giant ionic lattice. The oppositely charged ions are strongly attracted to each other and arrange themselves in a cube-shaped structure.

A single crystal of sodium chloride contains millions of ions arranged in this lattice pattern. It takes large amounts of energy to break the structure down when the crystals are melted.

Some ionic crystals need even more energy than sodium chloride to melt them. A stronger electrostatic attraction between the ions means a higher melting point and boiling point. The attraction is bigger when the ions have a larger charge.

For example, magnesium oxide has a higher melting point than sodium chloride because the magnesium ion has a 2+ charge and the oxide ion has a 2− charge. So the attraction between the magnesium and oxide ions is greater.

Quick Test

1. Atom X forms an ion by losing three electrons. What is the formulae of an ion of X?
2. Define 'oxidation' in terms of electrons.
3. Calcium reacts with fluorine to form the ionic compound calcium fluoride. What is the formulae of the ions present in calcium fluoride?
4. Give two properties of ionic compounds.
5. P2 Why does aluminium oxide have a higher melting point than sodium chloride?

Key Words   **Ionic compound**

The Covalent Bond

A **covalent bond** occurs between **non-metal atoms**. It is a strong bond, formed when **pairs of electrons are shared**. The strong attraction in the bond is between the shared pair of electrons and the nuclei of the two atoms.

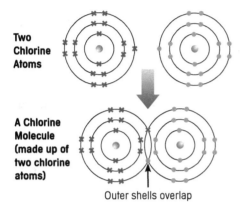

Two Chlorine Atoms

A Chlorine Molecule (made up of two chlorine atoms)

Outer shells overlap

Some covalently bonded substances have **simple structures**, e.g. H_2, Cl_2, O_2, HCl, H_2O and CH_4.

Others have **giant covalent structures**, called **macromolecules**, e.g. diamond and silicon dioxide.

Simple covalent structures usually have **low melting and boiling points**. This is because they often form molecules in which there are:
- **strong covalent bonds** between the **atoms**
- **weak forces of attraction** between the **molecules**.

The forces of attraction between the molecules are very weak compared to the strength of covalent bonds and therefore simple covalent substances are often gases and liquids at room temperature, or solids with low melting points.

Giant covalent molecules have much higher melting and boiling points because a large number of strong covalent bonds must be broken to break the giant structure apart.

P2 Carbon

Carbon exists in two giant covalent structures – **diamond** and **graphite**. The two structures have very different properties due to the way that the carbon atoms are arranged.

Diamond is made of carbon atoms bonded to four other carbon atoms by strong **covalent bonds**:
- Diamond is used in cutting tools because it's very hard and has a high melting point due to the large number of covalent bonds. These bonds need a lot of energy to break.

Graphite is made of layers of carbon atoms that are bonded to three other carbon atoms by strong **covalent bonds**:
- It's slippery, so it's used as a lubricant. The layers are held together by weak intermolecular forces, allowing each layer to slide easily.
- It has a high melting point because it has many strong covalent bonds to break. These bonds need a lot of energy to break.

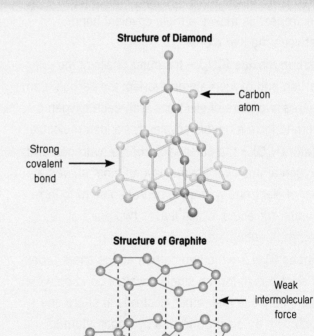

Structure of Diamond

Carbon atom

Strong covalent bond

Structure of Graphite

Weak intermolecular force

Strong covalent bond

Carbon atom

Covalent Substances

Simple Covalent Molecules

You should be familiar with how simple covalently bonded molecules are formed.

Hydrogen (H₂) – the two hydrogen atoms share a pair of electrons.

Chlorine (Cl₂) – the two chlorine atoms share a pair of electrons.

Hydrogen chloride (HCl) – the hydrogen and chlorine atoms share a pair of electrons.

Methane (CH₄) – the carbon atom shares a pair of electrons with each hydrogen atom.

Ammonia (NH₃) – each hydrogen atom shares a pair of electrons with the nitrogen atom, but the nitrogen atom still has a pair of electrons left over which it does not use for bonding.

Oxygen (O₂) – the two oxygen atoms share two pairs of electrons to create a double covalent bond between the two atoms.

Nitrogen (N₂) – the two nitrogen atoms must share three pairs of electrons to obtain a full shell of electrons; this makes a triple covalent bond between the two atoms.

Carbon dioxide (CO₂) – the outer shells of the carbon and oxygen atoms overlap; the carbon atom shares two pairs of electrons with each oxygen atom to form a double covalently bonded molecule.

Water (H₂O) – the outer shells of the hydrogen and oxygen atoms overlap; the oxygen atom shares a pair of electrons with each hydrogen atom to form a water molecule, which leaves two pairs of electrons unbonded.

Ethane (C₂H₆) – the two carbon atoms share a pair of electrons to form a single covalent bond between them; they use their other electrons to share one each with an electron from a hydrogen atom to form single covalent bonds.

Ethene (C₂H₄) – the two carbon atoms share two pairs of electrons to form a double covalent bond between them; they use their other electrons to share one each with an electron from a hydrogen atom to form single covalent bonds.

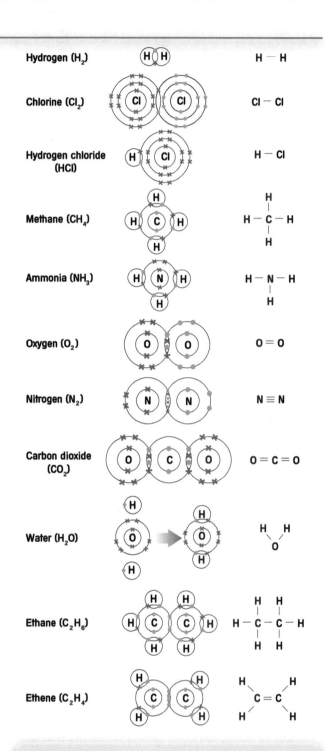

Quick Test

1. What is a covalent bond?
2. Why do simple covalent structures have relatively low melting points?
3. P2 Explain why graphite and diamond have high melting points.
4. Draw a dot and cross diagram to show the covalent bonds in methane (CH₄).

Properties of Metals

A metal has a **giant structure** of **ions** that is held together by strong forces of attraction called **metallic bonds**.

In a metal, the positively charged metal ions are held strongly together by a **'sea' of delocalised electrons**.

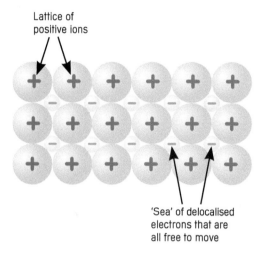

Lattice of positive ions

'Sea' of delocalised electrons that are all free to move

Metals:

- are **strong** – the ions are closely packed in a lattice structure
- have **high melting points** – a lot of energy is needed to break the strong metallic bonds.

Metals are also:

- **malleable** – they can be beaten into shape or dented as the layers of metal ions can slide over each other and the delocalised electrons prevent the metal cations (positive ions) getting too close to each other
- **conductors of electricity** – electrons are free to move throughout the structure. When a voltage is applied, the electrons move through the metal in one direction.

Quick Test

1. Why are metals able to conduct electricity?
2. Explain why metals are malleable.

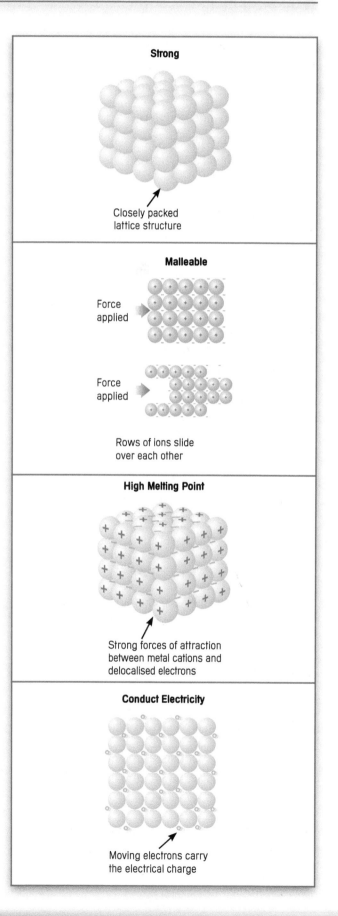

Strong

Closely packed lattice structure

Malleable

Force applied

Force applied

Rows of ions slide over each other

High Melting Point

Strong forces of attraction between metal cations and delocalised electrons

Conduct Electricity

Moving electrons carry the electrical charge

Electrolysis

Understanding Electrolysis

An electric current is the flow of electrons through a conductor but it can also flow by the movement of ions through a solution or a liquid.

Covalent compounds do not contain free electrons or ions that can move. So they will not conduct electricity when solid, liquid, gas or in solution.

The **ions** in:
- an **ionic solid** are fixed and can't move
- an **ionic substance** that is **molten** or in **solution** are free to move.

Electrolysis is a chemical reaction in which an ionic liquid is broken down (**decomposed**) into new substances using an **electric current**. It is a flow of charge produced by moving ions and ions are discharged at the electrodes.

The ionic substance is called the electrolyte.

The electrolyte must be molten or in solution as the ions need to be free to move:
- The positive ions (**cations**) move to, and discharge at, the negative electrode (cathode).
- The negative ions (**anions**) move to, and discharge at, the positive electrode (anode).

Electrons are removed from negative ions.

The electrons then flow around the circuit to the negative electrode and are passed to the positive ions.

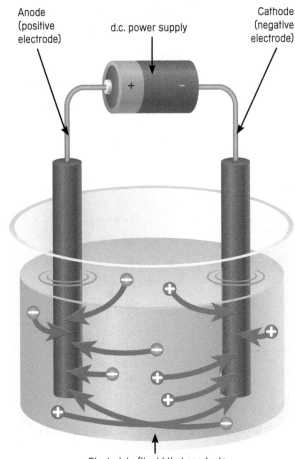

Anode (positive electrode)

d.c. power supply

Cathode (negative electrode)

Electrolyte (liquid that conducts and decomposes in electrolysis)

Testing Electrolytes

The apparatus shown here can be used to test liquids and solutions to determine if they conduct electricity.

An electrolyte will conduct electricity and the bulb will light. The electrolyte will contain ions that can move between the electrodes.

A non-electrolyte will not conduct electricity and the bulb will not light. The non-electrolyte does not contain ions.

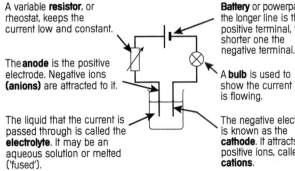

A variable **resistor**, or rheostat, keeps the current low and constant.

The **anode** is the positive electrode. Negative ions (**anions**) are attracted to it.

The liquid that the current is passed through is called the **electrolyte**. It may be an aqueous solution or melted ('fused').

Battery or powerpack – the longer line is the positive terminal, the shorter one the negative terminal.

A **bulb** is used to show the current is flowing.

The negative electrode is known as the **cathode**. It attracts positive ions, called **cations**.

Electrolysis • Electrolyte • Cathode • Anode

Electrolysis of a Molten Salt

When an ionic compound melts, electrostatic forces between the charged ions in the crystal lattice are broken down and the ions are free to move.

When a direct current is passed through a molten ionic compound:

- positively charged ions are attracted towards the **negative electrode**
- negatively charged ions are attracted towards the **positive electrode**.

For example, in the electrolysis of molten lead bromide:

- positively charged lead ions are attracted towards the **negative electrode**, forming lead (a metal)
- negatively charged bromide ions are attracted towards the **positive electrode**, forming bromine (a non-metal).

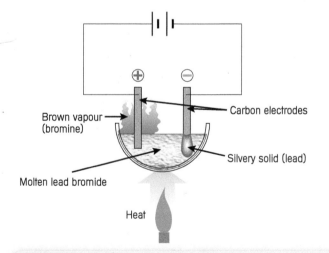

Brown vapour (bromine)

Carbon electrodes

Silvery solid (lead)

Molten lead bromide

Heat

When ions get to the oppositely charged electrode they're **discharged**, i.e. they lose their charge.

For example, in the electrolysis of molten lead bromide, the non-metal ion loses electrons to the positive electrode to form a bromine atom. The bromine atom then bonds with a second atom to form a bromine molecule.

The reactions at the electrodes can be written as **half equations**. This means that you write separate equations for what is happening in terms of electrons at each of the electrodes during electrolysis.

Bromide ions lose electrons at the positive electrode and form bromine molecules:

$$2Br^- \longrightarrow Br_2 + 2e^-$$

or $\quad 2Br^- - 2e^- \longrightarrow Br_2$

The lead ions gain electrons from the negative electrode to form a lead atom:

$$Pb^{2+} + 2e^- \longrightarrow Pb$$

This process completes the circuit as the electrons are exchanged at the electrodes.

Quick Test

1. Why do covalent substances not conduct electricity?
2. Why must electrolytes be in the liquid state?
3. Molten sodium chloride consists of Na^+ ions and Cl^- ions. What happens to these ions when a direct current is passed through molten sodium chloride?
4. Complete the following half equations:

   a) $Al^{3+} + \text{............} \longrightarrow Al$

   b) $2Cl^- \longrightarrow Cl_2 + \text{............}$

Electrolysis

Electrolysis of Aqueous Solutions

When a solution undergoes electrolysis, there is also water present. The ions created by water (H^+ and OH^-) are often discharged.

At the cathode, H^+ ions will be discharged, forming hydrogen gas, unless the metal cation present is below hydrogen in the reactivity series. At the anode, OH^- ions will be discharged, forming oxygen gas, unless a halide ion is present.

Electrolysis of Sodium Chloride Solution

In the electrolysis of sodium chloride solution (brine) hydrogen gas is produced at the cathode (because hydrogen is below sodium in the reactivity series) and chlorine is formed at the anode due to the presence of chloride ions. This means sodium ions and hydroxide ions remain in solution, forming sodium hydroxide solution.

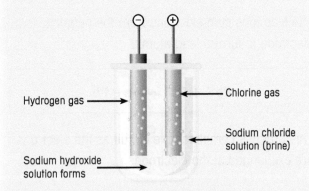

Hydrogen gas

Chlorine gas

Sodium chloride solution (brine)

Sodium hydroxide solution forms

This is the reaction at the **cathode**:

$$2H^+ + 2e^- \longrightarrow H_2$$

This is the reaction at the **anode**:

$$2Cl^- \longrightarrow Cl_2 + 2e^-$$

The electrolysis of sodium chloride solution is used in industry to make large quantities of very important chemicals: chlorine, sodium hydroxide and hydrogen (see page 95).

Electrolysis of Copper(II) Sulfate Solution

When an electric current is passed through copper(II) sulfate ($CuSO_4$) solution using inert electrodes:

- at the positive electrode bubbles form as oxygen is made
- the negative electrode becomes plated with copper and the mass increases
- the electrolyte becomes less blue as copper(II) sulfate is used up.

This is the reaction at the **cathode**:

$$Cu^{2+} + 2e^- \longrightarrow Cu$$

This is the reaction at the **anode**:

$$4OH^- \longrightarrow O_2 + 2H_2O + 4e^-$$

Electrolysis of Sulfuric Acid

When dilute sulfuric acid undergoes electrolysis:

- the hydrogen cations are attracted to the cathode and form hydrogen gas
- the hydroxide anions are attracted to the anode and form oxygen gas.

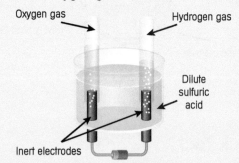

Oxygen gas

Hydrogen gas

Dilute sulfuric acid

Inert electrodes

This is the reaction at the **cathode**:

$$2H^+ + 2e^- \longrightarrow H_2$$

This is the reaction at the **anode**:

$$4OH^- \longrightarrow O_2 + 2H_2O + 4e^-$$

Amount of Product Made in Electrolysis

The amount of substance made in electrolysis is determined by the size of the current and the length of time it flows for.

More substance is made if:
- a larger current flows
- the current flows for a longer time.

The quantity of electricity (Q) passed in an electrolysis reaction can be calculated using the following formula:

Quantity of electricity (coulombs)	=	Current (amps)	×	Time (seconds)
$Q = I \times t$				

One mole of a substance with a 1^+ charge can be deposited by 96 500 coulombs. This quantity of electricity is the equivalent of passing 1 mole of electrons and is called 1 **faraday**.

1 faraday = 1 mole of electrons = 96 500 coulombs

- Passing 1 faraday (1 × 96 500 coulombs) will deposit 1 mole of a 1^+ ion (or a 1^- ion).
- Passing 2 faradays (2 × 96 500 coulombs) will deposit 1 mole of a 2^+ ion (or a 2^- ion).
- 3 faradays will be needed to discharge 1 mole of a 3^+ ion, etc.

This information can be used to calculate how much of a substance will be made from the current, and the time the electricity has been on.

Example 1

How many moles of silver are deposited when a solution containing Ag^+ ions is electrolysed for 24 125 seconds by a current of 2 amps?

$Q = I \times t$

$= 2 \times 24\ 125 = 48\ 250$ coulombs

Number of moles $= \dfrac{48\ 250}{96\ 500} = 0.5$ moles of electrons

0.5 moles of electrons = 0.5 faraday

As silver is a 1^+ ion then 0.5 faraday will deposit **0.5 moles Ag**

Example 2

What mass of copper will be deposited when copper(II) sulfate solution is electrolysed by a current of 5 amps for 193 seconds? *N.B. copper forms 2^+ ions.*

$Q = I \times t = 5 \times 193 = 965$ coulombs

Number of moles $= \dfrac{965}{96\ 500} = 0.01$ moles of electrons

0.01 moles of electrons = 0.01 faraday

As copper is a 2^+ ion then 2 faradays will deposit 1 mole Cu

So 0.01 faraday will deposit $\dfrac{0.01}{2} = 0.005$ moles Cu

Mass of copper made = No. of moles × A_r

$= 0.005 \times 63.5$

$= $ **0.3175g**

Quick Test

1. What are the three products of the electrolysis of sodium chloride solution?
2. What is produced at each electrode when copper(II) sulfate solution is electrolysed?
3. What is produced at each electrode when dilute sulfuric acid is electrolysed?
4. How many moles of sodium are deposited when a solution containing Na^+ ions is electrolysed for 25 minutes by a current of 4 amps?
5. What mass of copper will be deposited when a solution of copper(II) sulfate is electrolysed for 30 minutes using a current of 1.6 amps?

Exam Practice Questions

1 The diagram below represents an atom of the element lithium.

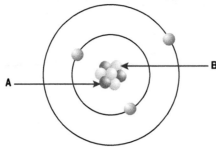

a) State the name of the particles labelled A and B. **[2]**

A - proton

B - neutron

b) What is the mass number of the atom shown above? Explain your answer. **[2]**

It has only one electron in it's outer shell
and hence the group number represents the
number

c) With reference to the above diagram, explain why lithium is in Group 1 of the Periodic Table. **[1]**

In a sample of lithium, 10% of atoms were the isotope lithium-6 and 90% were the isotope lithium-7.

d) What is meant by the term **isotopes**? **[2]**

Isotopes are atoms of the same element
that have the same ~~mass~~ atomic number but a
different mass number.

e) Calculate the relative atomic mass of this sample of lithium. **[3]**

Relat ~~(10×7) (90×6)~~ = 6.+
  ~~100~~   (10 x 6 +~~90×7~~) = 6.9
              100

f) Describe the structure of a metal such as lithium. You can draw a labelled diagram if you prefer. **[2]**

Lithium has a giant structures
of ions that is held together by strong forces of attraction
called metallic bonds. The positively charged metal ions are held
together by a sea of delocalised electrons.

g) Explain why metals such as lithium are good conductors of electricity. **[1]**

Electrons in the metal are free to move and
when a voltage is applied, electrons move through the metal in
one direction.

2 When carbon completely reacts with oxygen, the gas carbon dioxide is formed. The equation for the reaction is shown below.

$$C(s) + O_2(g) \longrightarrow CO_2(g)$$

a) With reference to the Periodic Table (see page 111), what is the relative formula mass (M_r) of carbon dioxide? **[1]**

$12 + 16 \times 2 = 44$

b) How many moles of carbon are there in 3g of carbon? **[1]**

$\text{moles} = \dfrac{3}{12} = 0.25\,\text{mol}$

c) What mass of carbon dioxide would be formed if 3g of carbon completely reacted with oxygen? **[2]**

$12 - C + O \longrightarrow CO_2 \quad = 44 \qquad 0.25 \times 44 = 11g$

$12 : 44$

$\dfrac{44}{100} \times 3 =$

P2 d) How many atoms of carbon are there in 3g of carbon? (Avogadro's number is 6×10^{23}) **[1]**

e) What volume of carbon dioxide would be formed if 3g of carbon completely reacted with oxygen? **[2]**

3 When magnesium reacts with oxygen, the compound magnesium oxide is formed.

a) What do you understand by the word **compound**? **[1]**

When atoms that are chemically combined are called compounds

b) Complete the diagram below to show the movement of electrons when an atom of magnesium reacts with an atom of oxygen. **[2]**

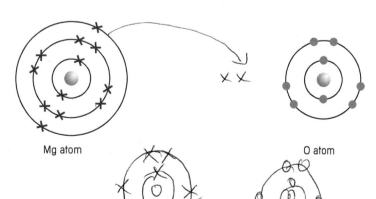

Mg atom   O atom

c) What is the charge on the magnesium ion formed when magnesium reacts with oxygen? **[1]**

Mg^{2+}

d) When magnesium reacts with oxygen, are the magnesium atoms oxidised or reduced? Explain your answer in terms of electrons. **[2]**

Magnesium are oxidised because magnesium loses two electrons.

e) Magnesium oxide contains ionic bonding. What is ionic bonding? **[2]**

Ionic bonding is when a metal and a non-metal combine for the transfer of electrons.

f) Explain why magnesium oxide has a high melting point. **[2]**

It has strong electrostatic forces between oppositely charged ions

P2 g) Sodium chloride (NaCl) is another compound that contains ionic bonding. Magnesium oxide has a higher melting point than sodium chloride. Explain why. **[2]**

4 Ammonia (NH_3) and diamond are two substances that contain covalent bonds. Ammonia has a simple covalent structure and diamond has a giant covalent structure.

a) What is meant by the term **covalent bond**? **[1]**

Covalent bond is a pair shared of pair of electrons between 2 atoms.

b) Draw a dot and cross diagram to show the bonds in a molecule of ammonia. The atomic number of nitrogen is 7 and the atomic number of hydrogen is 1. **[2]**

c) Ammonia is a gas at room temperature and pressure. Explain why simple covalent substances, such as ammonia, have low melting and boiling points. **[2]**

The forces of attraction between the molecules are very weak and this results in low melting and boiling points.

d) Explain why diamond has a high melting and boiling point. **[2]**

There are lots of strong covalent bonds.

5 A student was investigating the electrolysis of different solutions using the circuit shown below.

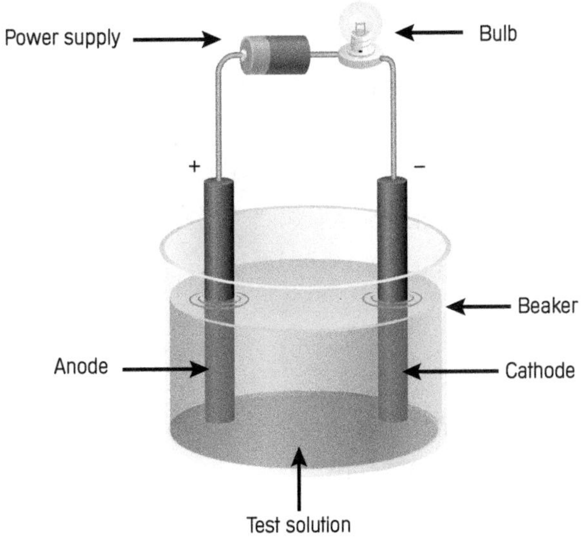

a) How will the student know whether the test solution conducts electricity? **[1]**

The bulb will light.

b) Sugar solution does not conduct electricity. What does this tell you about the type of bonding present in sugar? **[1]**

There are no ions to carry the charge it is covalent.

c) Copper(II) sulfate solution conducts electricity but solid copper(II) sulfate does not. Explain why. **[1]**

~~It must be molten~~ The ions in solid copper sulfate are not able to move however the ~~solids~~ ions in solution are free to move & carry the charge

P2 d) What is produced at the anode and the cathode during the electrolysis of copper(II) sulfate solution? **[2]**

33

The Periodic Table

Using the Periodic Table

An **element** is made of only one kind of **atom**. All the atoms of an element have the same number of **protons**.

Different **elements** have different **proton** (or atomic) **numbers** and they're arranged in order of increasing proton number in the **modern Periodic Table**. This gives repeating **patterns** in the **properties** of elements.

You can use the Periodic Table as a reference table to find out an element's:

- relative atomic mass (mass number) – the total number of protons and **neutrons** in an atom
- symbol
- name
- atomic (proton) number – the number of protons (and also the number of **electrons**) in an atom.

You can also tell if elements are **metals** or **non-metals** by looking at their position in the table.

N.B. *You will be given a copy of the Periodic Table in the exam. You can find one on page 111 of this book.*

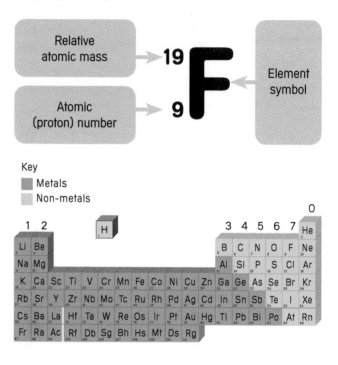

Groups

A **vertical column** of elements is called a **group**.

Group 1 elements include:

- lithium (Li)
- sodium (Na)
- potassium (K).

The group number corresponds to the number of electrons in the outer shell of an atom.

For example:

- **Group 1** elements have **one electron** in their outer shell
- **Group 7** elements have **seven electrons** in their outer shell.
- **Group O** elements have a **full outer shell**.

Elements that are in the same group have **similar properties** because they have the same number of electrons in their outer shell.

Periods

A **horizontal row** of elements is called a **period**. Examples of elements in the same period are lithium (Li), carbon (C) and neon (Ne).

The period number corresponds to how many shells there are in an atom of a particular element. For example, elements with three shells are found in the third period.

Key Words   Element • Atom • Proton • Neutron • Electron • Group • Period

Metals and Non-metals

Elements in the Periodic Table can be classed as metals, non-metals or metalloids. Metalloids are elements which show some properties of metals and some of non-metals. Antimony is an example of a metalloid.

Metals appear on the left and middle of the Periodic Table. Non-metals are to the right-hand side. They have quite different physical and chemical properties.

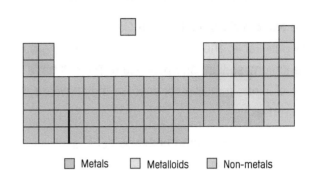

☐ Metals   ☐ Metalloids   ☐ Non-metals

Physical Properties

Metals are very useful materials because of their properties. They:

- are **lustrous** (shiny)
- are **hard** and have a high density
- have **high melting and boiling points** (except mercury and the alkali metals)
- are **good conductors of heat and electricity**
- are **malleable** (they can be hammered into shape)
- are **ductile** (they can be drawn into wires)
- are **sonorous** (they ring when struck).

Non-metals have very different properties. They:

- have **low melting points and boiling points** (except carbon and silicon)
- are **poor conductors of heat and electricity** (except graphite, a form of carbon, which is a good electrical conductor)
- are **brittle**
- are **dull**.

Chemical Properties

When elements react with oxygen, they form **oxides**.

Metals form **basic oxides**. If they are soluble in water, they will form **alkalis**. Insoluble metal oxides can react with acids to form salts.

Non-metals form **acidic oxides**. They form **acids** if they dissolve in water. Non-metal oxides, like sulfur dioxide and nitrogen dioxide, are responsible for causing acid rain.

The Noble Gases

Group O contains the noble gases. They all have stable electronic configurations. This means they have full outer shells so do not need to react with other elements. They are very **unreactive** (or inert).

Helium atom   Neon atom   Argon atom

Quick Test

1. What name is given to a horizontal row of elements in the Periodic Table?
2. Which side of the Periodic Table contains the metals?
3. Why do elements in the same group have similar chemical properties?
4. An element reacts with oxygen to form an acidic oxide. Is this element a metal or a non-metal?
5. Why are the noble gases inert?

Group 1 Elements

The Alkali Metals

The **alkali metals** are found in Group 1 of the Periodic Table. The first three elements in the group are lithium, sodium and potassium. They all have one electron in their outer shell, so they have **similar properties**.

Alkali metals are stored **under oil** because they:
- react with air
- react vigorously with water.

Alkali metals are shiny when freshly cut, but they quickly **tarnish in moist air**, go dull and become covered in a layer of metal oxide.

Sodium Metal

Reactions with Water

Alkali metals react with water to produce **hydrogen gas** and a metal hydroxide. Alkali metal hydroxides are soluble and form alkaline solutions, which is why Group 1 metals are known as **alkali** metals.

When lithium, sodium and potassium react with cold water, they:
- float (due to their low density)
- move around on the surface
- produce bubbles of hydrogen gas.

The alkali metals react more vigorously as you go down the group:
- Lithium reacts gently.
- Sodium reacts more aggressively than lithium. It melts and sometimes ignites to produce a yellow flame.
- Potassium reacts more aggressively than sodium – it melts and burns with a lilac flame.

Alkali Metals Reacting with Water

Li   Na   K

lithium **+** water $\longrightarrow$ lithium hydroxide **+** hydrogen

$$2Li(s) + 2H_2O(l) \longrightarrow 2LiOH(aq) + H_2(g)$$

sodium **+** water $\longrightarrow$ sodium hydroxide **+** hydrogen

$$2Na(s) + 2H_2O(l) \longrightarrow 2NaOH(aq) + H_2(g)$$

potassium **+** water $\longrightarrow$ potassium hydroxide **+** hydrogen

$$2K(s) + 2H_2O(l) \longrightarrow 2KOH(aq) + H_2(g)$$

Properties of the Alkali Metals

Alkali metals have similar chemical and physical properties.

Alkali metals:
- have **low** melting and boiling points that **decrease** as you go down the group
- have a **low** density (lithium, sodium and potassium are less dense than water)
- become **more reactive** as you go down the group.

Rubidium is the fourth element in Group 1. Rubidium's reaction with water is:
- very fast
- **exothermic** (gives out energy).

When rubidium reacts with water, rubidium hydroxide and hydrogen gas are formed.

Caesium has the greatest density, and lowest melting and boiling points. Caesium explodes on contact with water and forms caesium hydroxide and hydrogen gas.

P2 Trends in Group 1

Alkali metals have similar chemical properties because as they react, each atom **loses** one **electron** from its outer shell. So, a **positive ion** with a stable electronic structure is made.

The alkali metals become **more reactive** as you go down the group because the outer shell gets **further away** from the positive attraction of the **nucleus**. This makes it easier for an atom to lose an electron from its outer shell.

In the diagram shown, the outer electron for lithium is in the second shell, so it is close to the nucleus.

The outer electron in sodium is located in the third shell. This is further away from the attraction of the nucleus. It is easier for sodium to lose its outer electron, so sodium is more reactive than lithium.

Lithium	Sodium	Potassium

More reactive

Hazards of Alkali Metals

Alkali metals carry hazard symbols. When working with Group 1 metals, you should:
- use small amounts of the metals
- wear safety glasses and use safety screens
- watch teacher demonstrations carefully
- avoid working near naked flames
- ensure that the metals are stored under oil and that the lids are always tightly secured.

Quick Test

1. Name the two products formed when sodium reacts with water. *hydroxide + water*
2. What is the trend in reactivity of the Group 1 metals as you go down the group?
3. What is observed when a small piece of lithium reacts with water?
4. P2 Why is potassium more reactive than sodium?

Group 7 Elements

The Halogens

The five non-metals in Group 7 are known as the **halogens**. They all have seven electrons in their outer shell, so they have similar chemical properties.

Fluorine, chlorine, bromine and iodine are halogens. At room temperature:
- chlorine is a green gas
- bromine is an orange liquid
- iodine is a grey solid.

Halogens react vigorously with **alkali metals** to form metal **halides**, for example:

lithium + chlorine ⟶ lithium chloride
$2Li(s) + Cl_2(g) \longrightarrow 2LiCl(s)$

Trends in Group 7

Halogens become less reactive as you go down the group because the outer electron shell gets further away from the attraction of the nucleus, and so an electron is **gained less easily**.

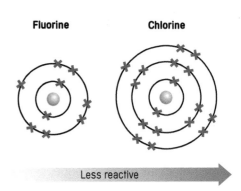

Fluorine   Chlorine

Less reactive

Properties of the Halogens

The physical and chemical properties of the halogens change as you go down the group.

The halogens:
- have melting and boiling points that **increase** as you go down the group (at room temperature, fluorine and chlorine are gases, and bromine is a liquid)
- have **coloured vapours** (chlorine's and bromine's vapours smell particularly strong)
- exist as **molecules** made up of **pairs of atoms**
- become **less reactive** as you go down the group.

Astatine is a semi-metallic, radioactive element and only very small amounts are found naturally.

Astatine is very unstable and difficult to study. So, the information for astatine is estimated by looking at the trends in boiling point, melting point and density as you go down Group 7.

Element	Symbol	Melting Point (°C)	Boiling Point (°C)	Density (g/cm³)
Fluorine	F	−220	−188	0.0016
Chlorine	Cl	−101	−34	0.003
Bromine	Br	−7	59	3.12
Iodine	I	114	184	4.95
Astatine	At	302 (estimated)	337 (estimated)	7 (estimated)

Key Words   Halogen • Halide

Displacement Reactions

The reactivity of the halogens decreases as you go down the group. So, fluorine is the most reactive halogen and astatine is the least reactive.

A **more reactive** halogen will **displace** a **less reactive** halogen from an aqueous solution of its metal halide. For example:

- chlorine will displace bromides and iodides
- bromine will displace iodides.

If chlorine gas was passed through an aqueous solution of potassium bromide, bromine and potassium chloride would be made in the displacement reaction.

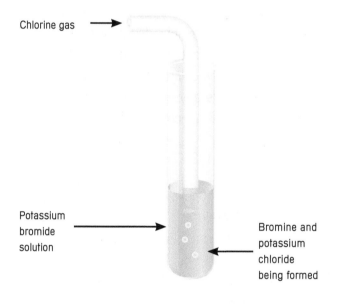

Chlorine gas

Potassium bromide solution

Bromine and potassium chloride being formed

The products of reactions between halogens and aqueous solutions of salts are as follows:

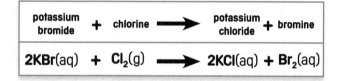

Halogen \ Halide salt	Potassium Chloride, KCl	Potassium Bromide, KBr	Potassium Iodide, KI
Chlorine, Cl_2	No reaction	potassium chloride + bromine	potassium chloride + iodine
Bromine, Br_2	No reaction	No reaction	potassium bromide + iodine
Iodine, I_2	No reaction	No reaction	No reaction

potassium bromide	+	chlorine	$\longrightarrow$	potassium chloride	+ bromine

$$2KBr(aq) + Cl_2(g) \longrightarrow 2KCl(aq) + Br_2(aq)$$

potassium iodide	+	chlorine	$\longrightarrow$	potassium chloride	+ iodine

$$2KI(aq) + Cl_2(g) \longrightarrow 2KCl(aq) + I_2(aq)$$

potassium iodide	+	bromine	$\longrightarrow$	potassium bromide	+ iodine

$$2KI(aq) + Br_2(l) \longrightarrow 2KBr(aq) + I_2(aq)$$

You may be asked to suggest if a displacement reaction will happen. Remember that chlorine is more reactive than bromine, which is more reactive than iodine.

Redox Reactions

In the displacement reaction described above, chlorine displaces bromine from potassium bromide solution.

Chlorine gas has gained electrons to form chloride ions.

$$Cl_2(g) + 2e^- \longrightarrow 2Cl^-(aq)$$

When electrons are gained, it is a **reduction** reaction.

Bromide ions lose electrons to the chlorine and form bromine.

$$2Br^-(aq) \longrightarrow Br_2(aq) + 2e^-$$

Loss of electrons is an **oxidation** reaction.

This is an example of a redox reaction, as the chlorine is reduced and the bromide is oxidised.

Group 7 Elements

Uses of Halogens

The halogens and their compounds have many uses:

- Fluoride is used in toothpaste to help prevent tooth decay.
- Chlorine is used to sterilise water, to make household bleaches and plastics.
- Bromine is used to make pesticides.
- Iodine is used as an antiseptic to sterilise wounds.

Hydrogen Chloride and Hydrochloric Acid

Another important use of chlorine is in the manufacture of hydrochloric acid. Hydrochloric acid is an important raw material in many industrial processes.

When chlorine reacts with hydrogen it makes hydrogen chloride gas.

hydrogen + chlorine $\longrightarrow$ hydrogen chloride
$H_2(g) + Cl_2(g) \longrightarrow 2HCl(g)$

Hydrochloric acid is then produced by dissolving hydrogen chloride in water (represented by aq), as shown below.

hydrogen chloride + water $\longrightarrow$ hydrochloric acid
$HCl(g) + aq \longrightarrow H^+(aq) + Cl^-(aq)$

After dissolving, the hydrogen ions and chloride ions **dissociate** in water. This means they can move independently as the individual ions have broken apart from each other.

acids bases accepts
HCl (g) + H₂O(l)

If hydrogen chloride is dissolved in methylbenzene (an organic solvent), the ions do not dissociate. The solution made contains hydrogen chloride molecules. Hydrogen chloride in methylbenzene does not behave like a typical acid. As no ions are present, it also does not conduct electricity.

Quick Test

1. Describe the appearance of bromine at room temperature.
2. What is the trend in reactivity of the halogens as you go down Group 7?
3. Which one of the following reactions will not occur?

   A: chlorine + potassium bromide $\longrightarrow$ potassium chloride + bromine

   B: iodine + potassium chloride $\longrightarrow$ potassium iodide + chlorine

   C: bromine + potassium iodide $\longrightarrow$ potassium bromide + iodine

4. Which one of the following is an oxidation reaction?

   A: $Cl_2 + 2e^- \longrightarrow 2Cl^-$

   B: $2Cl^- \longrightarrow Cl_2 + 2e^-$

5. Why does HCl dissolved in methylbenzene not behave like a typical acid?

Composition of the Atmosphere

The percentage by volume of gases in the atmosphere has been more or less the same for about 200 million years. The percentages are shown in the pie chart.

Water vapour may also be present in varying quantities (0–3%).

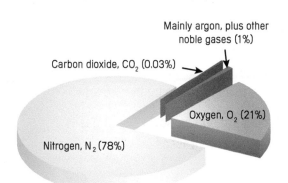

Mainly argon, plus other noble gases (1%)

Carbon dioxide, CO_2 (0.03%)

Oxygen, O_2 (21%)

Nitrogen, N_2 (78%)

Determining the Percentage of Oxygen in Air

It is possible to show the composition of oxygen in air by conducting simple laboratory experiments.

By reacting copper, iron or phosphorus with a specific volume of air, the volume will decrease as oxygen reacts.

Copper reacts with oxygen to form black copper(II) oxide powder.

copper + oxygen $\longrightarrow$ copper(II) oxide
$2Cu(s) + O_2(g) \longrightarrow 2CuO(s)$

This reaction happens in the experiment below:

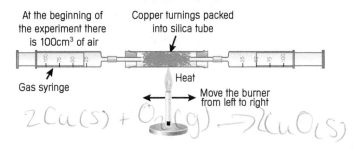

At the beginning of the experiment there is 100cm³ of air

Copper turnings packed into silica tube

Gas syringe

Heat

Move the burner from left to right

$2Cu(s) + O_2(g) \rightarrow 2CuO(s)$

At the start of the experiment, one syringe contains 100cm³ of air and the other is empty. The air is passed from one syringe to the other, over the copper metal as it is heated. The oxygen in the air reacts with the copper, forming copper(II) oxide.

As the reaction progresses, the volume of air will decrease as the copper(II) oxide forms. The experiment is finished once the volume stops

decreasing. The volume goes down to about 79cm³. This means the 100cm³ of air at the start must have contained 21cm³ of oxygen, in other words 21% oxygen.

The experiment uses copper, but iron filings could be used as an alternative to copper.

An alternative experiment uses water to displace the oxygen as it reacts. This approach was used by early chemists to find the amount of oxygen in air.

In the following experiment, phosphorus reacts with oxygen to form phosphorus(V) oxide.

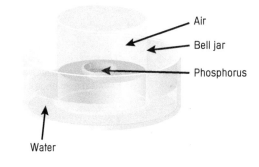

Air

Bell jar

Phosphorus

Water

phosphorus + oxygen $\longrightarrow$ phosphorus(V) oxide
$4P(s) + 5O_2(g) \longrightarrow 2P_2O_5(s)$

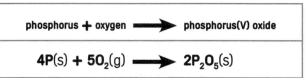

As the oxygen reacts, the water rises up inside the bell jar to replace it. It stops rising after all the oxygen is used up. By marking the water level at the start and end of the experiment, the water should have displaced about one-fifth of the air.

Oxygen and Oxides

Laboratory Preparation of Oxygen

Hydrogen peroxide slowly decomposes to form oxygen gas and water. This reaction is used to obtain oxygen in a laboratory. A catalyst of manganese(IV) oxide is used to speed up the process.

The diagram shows how oxygen gas is collected as the reaction progresses.

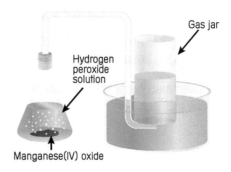

Reactions with Oxygen

When an element reacts with oxygen, the reaction is called an **oxidation reaction**. Many elements will react if heated in air.

When magnesium burns in oxygen, it produces an intense bright white light which should not be looked at directly.

magnesium + oxygen $\longrightarrow$ magnesium oxide
$2Mg(s) + O_2(g) \longrightarrow 2MgO(s)$

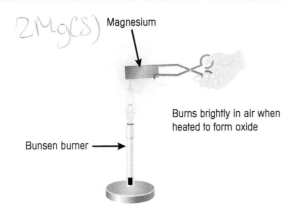

$2MgCS)$

Magnesium

Burns brightly in air when heated to form oxide

Bunsen burner

Magnesium oxide is a white powder. It forms an **alkaline** solution if distilled water is added to it.

All metal oxides are **basic oxides**. If soluble, they dissolve in water to form alkaline solutions with a pH greater than 7.

Sulfur burns in oxygen to form colourless sulfur dioxide gas. The sulfur burns with a blue flame.

sulfur + oxygen $\longrightarrow$ sulfur dioxide
$S(s) + O_2(g) \longrightarrow SO_2(g)$

When sulfur dioxide dissolves in distilled water, the resulting solution is **acidic**.

Sulfur is an example of a non-metal. All non-metal oxides are **acidic oxides**. If soluble, they dissolve in water and form solutions with a pH less than 7.

Carbon burns in air to form colourless carbon dioxide gas.

carbon + oxygen $\longrightarrow$ carbon dioxide
$2C(s) + O_2(g) \longrightarrow CO_2(g)$

Quick Test

1. Approximately how much of the air is oxygen?
2. Oxygen can be made in a laboratory from hydrogen peroxide. What catalyst is used in this process?
3. What is observed when sulfur burns in oxygen?
4. Sulfur dioxide dissolved in distilled water forms an _____ solution.

Laboratory Preparation of Carbon Dioxide

Reacting a Metal Carbonate with Acid

Carbon dioxide is prepared in a laboratory by reacting hydrochloric acid with a metal carbonate, usually calcium carbonate.

calcium carbonate	+	hydrochloric acid	→	carbon dioxide	+ water +	calcium chloride

$$CaCO_3(s) + 2HCl(aq) \rightarrow CO_2(g) + H_2O(l) + CaCl_2(aq)$$

As with oxygen gas, carbon dioxide is collected by displacement of water.

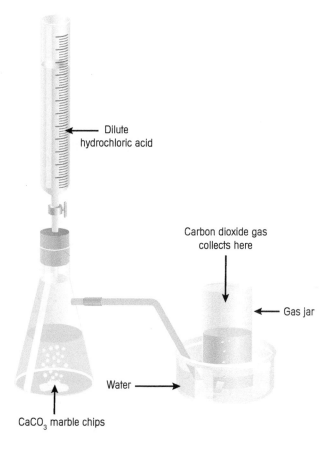

Dilute hydrochloric acid

Carbon dioxide gas collects here

← Gas jar

Water →

$CaCO_3$ marble chips

Thermally Decomposing a Metal Carbonate

Carbon dioxide can also be obtained through the **thermal decomposition** of metal carbonates.

Green copper(II) carbonate decomposes on heating to produce black copper(II) oxide and carbon dioxide gas.

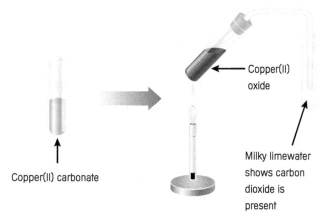

Copper(II) oxide

Milky limewater shows carbon dioxide is present

Copper(II) carbonate

copper(II) carbonate	→	copper(II) oxide +	carbon dioxide

$$CuCO_3(s) \rightarrow CuO(s) + CO_2(g)$$

Examples of the thermal decomposition of other metal carbonates are:

zinc carbonate	→	zinc oxide + carbon dioxide

$$ZnCO_3(s) \rightarrow ZnO(s) + CO_2(g)$$

iron(II) carbonate	→	iron(II) oxide + carbon dioxide

$$FeCO_3(s) \rightarrow FeO(s) + CO_2(g)$$

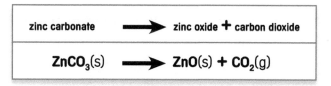

manganese carbonate	→	manganese oxide +	carbon dioxide

$$MnCO_3(s) \rightarrow MnO(s) + CO_2(g)$$

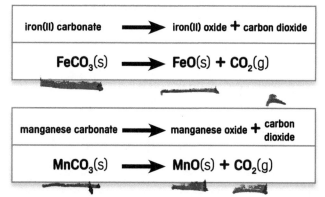

Oxygen and Oxides

Properties and Reactions of Carbon Dioxide

Carbon dioxide is a colourless gas. It is more dense than air and is slightly soluble in water. It can also react with water to produce carbonic acid. This explains why rainwater is naturally slightly acidic.

Uses of Carbon Dioxide

Carbon dioxide is used in some fire extinguishers. As it is more dense than air, it covers the fire and stops oxygen getting to it. Carbon dioxide does not burn so the fire goes out.

Carbon dioxide is also used to make fizzy drinks (or carbonated drinks). It is only slightly soluble in water but it is added to drinks under pressure, which increases its solubility. When cans or bottles are opened, the pressure is released and the carbon dioxide fizzes out.

Carbon Dioxide and Climate Change

There is a concern that carbon dioxide and other greenhouse gases are responsible for **global warming**. Greenhouse gases stop heat energy leaving the Earth's atmosphere and so keep the planet warmer than it would otherwise be.

In May 2013, measurements at the Mauna Loa test station in Hawaii measured carbon dioxide at 0.04% of the air for the first time.

Many scientists believe the levels of carbon dioxide are increasing due to the excessive burning of fossil fuels and large-scale deforestation. By removing trees, there is less photosynthesis happening to remove carbon dioxide from the atmosphere.

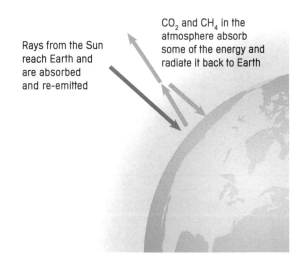

Rays from the Sun reach Earth and are absorbed and re-emitted

CO_2 and CH_4 in the atmosphere absorb some of the energy and radiate it back to Earth

Quick Test

1. Which gas is produced when calcium carbonate reacts with hydrochloric acid?
2. Upon heating, copper(II) carbonate turns into copper(II) oxide and carbon dioxide. What name is given to this type of reaction?
3. Give two uses of carbon dioxide gas.
4. Which environmental problem do greenhouse gases contribute to?

Reacting Metals with Acids

Many metals react with dilute acids and produce a salt and hydrogen gas.

Metal + Acid ⟶ Salt + Hydrogen

Some metals are more reactive than others and the strength of the reaction will depend on the metal used.

The diagram opposite shows that of the metals shown (reacting with the same volume and concentration of acid in each case), magnesium is the most reactive and iron is the least reactive. The reaction of magnesium with acid is producing more bubbles of hydrogen gas than the other metals. Iron with acid has the fewest bubbles.

Examples of equations include:

magnesium + hydrochloric acid ⟶ magnesium chloride + hydrogen

$$Mg(s) + 2HCl(aq) \longrightarrow MgCl_2(aq) + H_2(g)$$

zinc + sulfuric acid ⟶ zinc sulfate + hydrogen

$$Zn(s) + H_2SO_4(aq) \longrightarrow ZnSO_4(aq) + H_2(g)$$

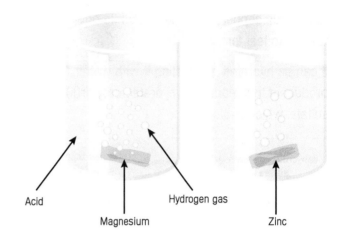

Acid — Magnesium — Hydrogen gas — Zinc

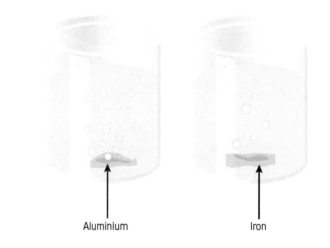

Aluminium — Iron

Combustion of Hydrogen

Hydrogen is a colourless gas which is less dense than air. It has the formula H_2. At room temperature, a mixture of hydrogen and oxygen will not react. If the mixture is heated or exposed to a flame, it will explode. This reaction between hydrogen and oxygen is an example of a **combustion** reaction and is very **exothermic**. The product of the reaction is water.

hydrogen + oxygen ⟶ water

$$2H_2(g) + O_2(g) \longrightarrow 2H_2O(l)$$

As this reaction is explosive, a test tube of hydrogen gas will make a 'pop' sound if a lighted splint is held in the mouth of the tube.

Hydrogen

Lighted splint

Hydrogen and Water

Testing for Water

Anhydrous copper(II) sulfate is a white powder and is used to test for water.

It can be hydrated by reacting it with water. The product of this reaction is hydrated copper(II) sulfate, which is blue.

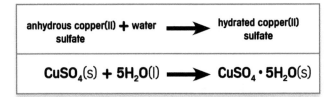

anhydrous copper(II) sulfate **+** water $\longrightarrow$ hydrated copper(II) sulfate

$$CuSO_4(s) + 5H_2O(l) \longrightarrow CuSO_4 \cdot 5H_2O(s)$$

An experiment can be set up as shown.

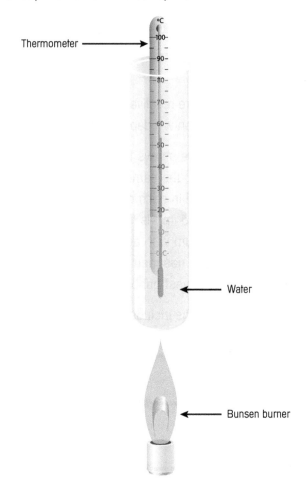

Thermometer

Water

Bunsen burner

Anhydrous copper(II) sulfate can't be used to check the purity of water. It will give a positive test even if the water contains impurities.

To check the purity of water, the boiling point of the water should be tested. Pure water boils at 100°C. If any impurities are in the water, the boiling point will increase.

A small sample of water should be used, and an accurate thermometer. As the temperature nears the expected value (100°C), the heating should be very gradual so the boiling point can be accurately determined. Impurities usually increase the boiling point by a few degrees Celsius.

Quick Test

1. What are the products of the reaction between zinc and sulfuric acid?
2. What is observed when hydrogen combusts?
3. What is observed when water is added to anhydrous copper(II) sulfate?
4. How can the purity of water be confirmed by a physical test?

Metals with Water and Acids

Metals with Water

Metals that react with water form hydrogen gas and either the metal hydroxide or the metal oxide. Some metals react more violently than others and some do not react at all:

- Potassium – very vigorous reaction.
- Calcium – vigorous reaction.
- Magnesium – no reaction with cold water but will react with steam.
- Copper – no reaction, even with steam.

metal + water ➡ hydrogen + metal hydroxide or metal oxide

potassium + water ➡ hydrogen + potassium hydroxide
$2K + 2H_2O \longrightarrow H_2 + 2KOH$

magnesium + steam ➡ hydrogen + magnesium oxide
$Mg + 2H_2O \longrightarrow H_2 + MgO$

Metals with Acids

Metals that react with dilute acids form hydrogen gas and a salt. Some metals react violently and some not at all:

- Potassium, sodium and lithium – very violent and dangerous reactions.
- Magnesium – vigorous reaction.
- Zinc – steady reaction.
- Copper – no reaction.

metal + acid ➡ hydrogen + a salt

magnesium + hydrochloric acid ➡ hydrogen + magnesium chloride
$Mg + 2HCl \longrightarrow H_2 + MgCl_2$

zinc + sulfuric acid ➡ hydrogen + zinc sulfate
$Zn + H_2SO_4 \longrightarrow H_2 + ZnSO_4$

Arranging Metals in Order of their Reactivity

The reactivity series puts metals in order of their reactivity, from the **most** to the **least reactive**. The position of a metal is based on how it reacts with water, acids and in competition with other metals.

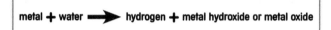

Metal	Reaction with water	Reaction with acid	Overall
Potassium	Increasing reactivity with cold water	Very violent reaction with dilute acid	Increasing reactivity
Sodium			
Lithium			
Calcium			
Magnesium	Increasing reactivity with steam	Increasing reactivity with dilute acid	
Aluminium			
Zinc			
Iron			
Copper	No reaction with water or steam	No reaction with dilute acid	
Silver			
Gold			

Reactivity Series

Displacement Reactions

A **displacement reaction** is one in which a more reactive metal displaces a less reactive metal from a compound. In other words, a metal higher up in the reactivity series will 'push out' a metal lower in the series.

For example, if an iron nail is put into a beaker of copper sulfate solution, then a displacement reaction occurs because iron is higher in the reactivity series than copper.

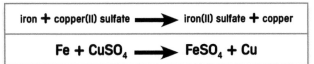

iron **+** copper(II) sulfate ⟶ iron(II) sulfate **+** copper

$$Fe + CuSO_4 \longrightarrow FeSO_4 + Cu$$

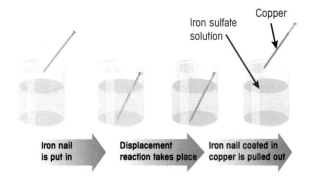

Iron sulfate solution   Copper

| Iron nail is put in | Displacement reaction takes place | Iron nail coated in copper is pulled out |

If the pure metal is higher in the reactivity series than the metal in the compound, the displacement will happen.

Using the Reactivity Series

If you know the position of a metal in the reactivity series, then you can make a prediction about:

- its reaction with water
- its reaction with dilute acids
- whether it will displace another metal in a compound.

Displacement reactions can be used to determine the position of a metal in the reactivity series.

Method 1: The metal can be tested against a range of metal salts dissolved in water. It will only displace the metal from the salt if it is more reactive. **For example:** Put a strip of the metal into each of the following solutions:

- No reaction when added to aluminium sulfate.
- No reaction when added to iron(II) sulfate.
- Copper is displaced onto the metal when added to copper(II) sulfate.

These results show that this metal is more reactive than copper but less reactive than iron, and fits in between these two metals in the reactivity series.

Method 2: The metal can be mixed with the oxides of different metals and then heated. It will only displace the metal from its oxide if it is more reactive.

For example: Mix the metal with a range of metal oxides and heat strongly:

- No reaction with aluminium oxide.
- Iron is produced with iron(II) oxide.
- Copper is produced with copper(II) oxide.

These results show that this metal is more reactive than copper and iron but less reactive than aluminium so, it fits in between iron and aluminium in the reactivity series.

Redox Reactions

There is an alternative way to define oxidation and reduction using oxygen:

- **Oxidation** is the addition of oxygen.
- **Reduction** is the removal of oxygen.

A **redox reaction** is when oxidation and reduction happen at the same time.

An **oxidising agent** adds oxygen onto another reactant. A **reducing agent** removes oxygen from another reactant.

Rusting

The diagram shows an investigation into the conditions needed to make a nail rust.

Three nails were placed in test tubes in different conditions and left for a week. The only nail that rusted was the one in test tube 3. From this we can tell that rusting needs iron, water and oxygen (in air). The addition of oxygen to the iron is an **oxidation reaction**.

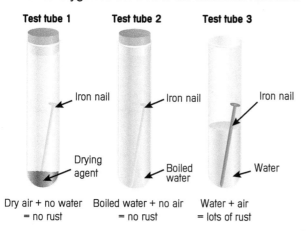

Test tube 1   **Test tube 2**   **Test tube 3**

Iron nail   Iron nail   Iron nail

Drying agent   Boiled water   Water

Dry air + no water = no rust   Boiled water + no air = no rust   Water + air = lots of rust

Oxygen is added to the iron in the presence of water.

iron **+** oxygen **+** water ⟶ hydrated iron(III) oxide (rust)

Rust flakes off the iron, exposing more metal to corrosion. Rusting happens even faster when the water is salty or is made from acid rain. Car bodies can rust. They are usually scrapped when this happens because it makes the metal weaker.

Stopping Rusting

Rusting can be prevented by coating the iron with materials that stop water and air coming into contact with the metal surface (barrier methods). Typical materials include paint, oil, grease and plastic.

Covering the iron with a thin coating of zinc metal also works as a barrier method. This is called **galvanising**. There is extra protection as zinc is higher in the reactivity series than iron, and if the surface is damaged the zinc will corrode (be oxidised) before the iron. This is a form of sacrificial corrosion, where a more reactive metal is sacrificed to protect a less reactive one.

Sacrificial protection is also used on large iron structures such as bridges or ships. Blocks of zinc or magnesium (both more reactive than iron) are attached to the structures and will corrode in place of the iron.

Quick Test

1. Name two metals that are more reactive than aluminium.
2. Magnesium displaces copper from copper(II) oxide. What can you deduce about the reactivity of magnesium compared with copper?
3. In the reaction between copper and oxygen forming copper(II) oxide, which substance is oxidised?
4. When magnesium reacts with copper(II) oxide, the products are magnesium oxide and copper. What is the reducing agent in this reaction?
5. State two ways by which rusting can be prevented.

Tests for Ions and Gases

Identifying Metal Ions (Cations)

Flame tests can be used to identify metal **ions**.

Lithium, sodium, potassium and calcium compounds can be recognised by the distinctive colours they produce in a **flame test**.

To do a flame test, follow this method:

1. Heat and then dip a piece of nichrome (a nickel-chromium alloy) wire in concentrated hydrochloric acid to clean it.
2. Dip the wire in the compound.
3. Put it into a Bunsen flame. Different colours will indicate the presence of certain ions.

The distinctive colours are:
- brick red for **calcium** (Ca^{2+})
- crimson red for **lithium** (Li^+)
- lilac for **potassium** (K^+)
- yellow for **sodium** (Na^+).

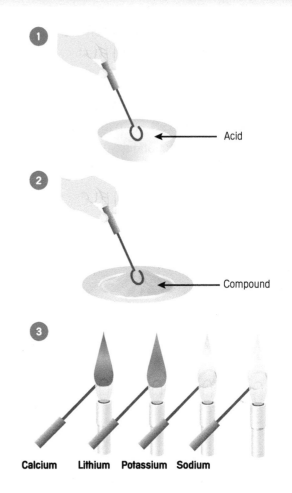

Identifying Ammonium Ions

Sodium hydroxide solution can be used to identify ammonium ions, NH_4^+.

To see if an unknown compound contains ammonium ions:

1. In a test tube, dissolve a sample of the compound in water
2. Add a few drops of dilute sodium hydroxide solution
3. Gently warm the mixture using a Bunsen burner
4. Hold a piece of damp red litmus paper in the mouth of the test tube.

If ammonium ions are present, the indicator paper will turn blue (alkaline) due to the formation of ammonia (NH_3) gas.

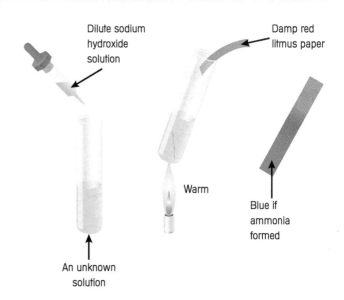

Identifying Metal Ions in Solution

Sodium hydroxide solution can also be used to test for metal ions in solution.

Metal compounds in solution contain **metal ions**. Some of these form **precipitates** (i.e. **insoluble** solids) that come out of solution when sodium hydroxide solution is added to them.

For example, when sodium hydroxide solution is added to copper(II) chloride solution, a blue precipitate of copper(II) hydroxide is formed (as well as sodium chloride solution).

You can see how this precipitate is formed by considering the ions involved. The table below shows the precipitates formed when **metal ions** are mixed with sodium hydroxide solution.

Metal Ion	Symbol	Colour of Precipitate	Equation
Copper(II)	Cu^{2+}	Blue	$Cu^{2+} + 2OH^- \longrightarrow Cu(OH)_2$
Iron(II)	Fe^{2+}	Green	$Fe^{2+} + 2OH^- \longrightarrow Fe(OH)_2$
Iron(III)	Fe^{3+}	Brown	$Fe^{3+} + 3OH^- \longrightarrow Fe(OH)_3$

The green iron(II) hydroxide precipitate, $Fe(OH)_2$, will be oxidised in air and slowly turn to brown iron(III) hydroxide, $Fe(OH)_3$.

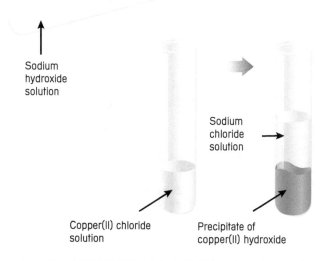

Sodium hydroxide solution

Sodium chloride solution

Copper(II) chloride solution

Precipitate of copper(II) hydroxide

Identifying Carbonate Ions

An unknown solid can be tested with dilute acid to see if it contains carbonate ions, CO_3^{2-}. If the solid is a carbonate, it will react with the acid to form a salt, water and carbon dioxide gas. For example:

calcium carbonate	+	hydrochloric acid	→	calcium chloride	+	carbon dioxide	+	water

$$CaCO_3(s) + 2HCl(aq) \longrightarrow CaCl_2(aq) + CO_2(g) + H_2O(l)$$

Limewater can be used to test for carbon dioxide. If the gas is present, the limewater will turn milky / cloudy.

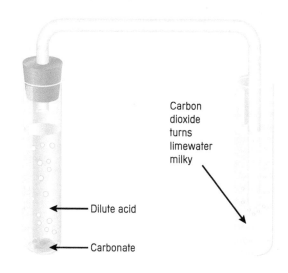

Carbon dioxide turns limewater milky

Dilute acid

Carbonate

Tests for Ions and Gases

Identifying Dissolved Ions

The **dissolved ions** of some salts are easy to identify as they will undergo **precipitation** reactions. A precipitation reaction occurs when an insoluble solid is made from mixing two solutions together.

Sulfates (SO_4^{2-}) can be detected using dilute hydrochloric acid and barium chloride solution. A white precipitate of barium sulfate forms, as in the following example:

| sodium sulfate | + | barium chloride | → | barium sulfate (white) | + | sodium chloride |

$$Na_2SO_4(aq) + BaCl_2(aq) \rightarrow BaSO_4(s) + 2NaCl(aq)$$

Silver nitrate solution, in the presence of dilute nitric acid, is used to detect halide ions. Halides are the ions made by the halogens (Group 7).

With silver nitrate:

- chlorides (Cl^-) form a white precipitate
- bromides (Br^-) form a cream precipitate
- iodides (I^-) form a pale yellow precipitate.

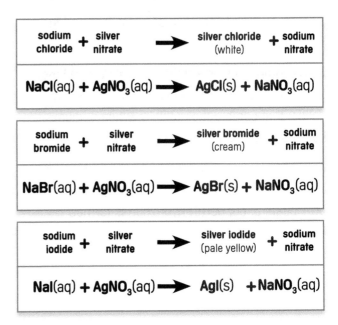

| sodium chloride | + | silver nitrate | → | silver chloride (white) | + | sodium nitrate |

$$NaCl(aq) + AgNO_3(aq) \rightarrow AgCl(s) + NaNO_3(aq)$$

| sodium bromide | + | silver nitrate | → | silver bromide (cream) | + | sodium nitrate |

$$NaBr(aq) + AgNO_3(aq) \rightarrow AgBr(s) + NaNO_3(aq)$$

| sodium iodide | + | silver nitrate | → | silver iodide (pale yellow) | + | sodium nitrate |

$$NaI(aq) + AgNO_3(aq) \rightarrow AgI(s) + NaNO_3(aq)$$

Chlorides form a white precipitate

Bromides form a cream precipitate

Iodides form a pale yellow precipitate

Testing for Gases

Testing for Hydrogen

Hydrogen burns with a squeaky pop when tested with a lighted splint.

Hydrogen

Lighted splint

Testing for Oxygen

Oxygen re-lights a glowing splint.

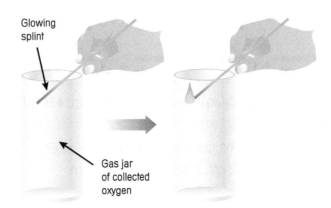

Glowing splint

Gas jar of collected oxygen

Testing for Gases (Cont.)

Testing for Carbon Dioxide

Carbon dioxide will turn limewater milky / cloudy.

This test can be used to show that carbon dioxide is produced when a metal carbonate is heated.

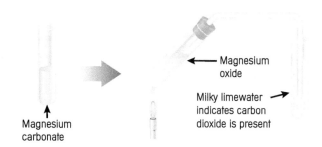

Magnesium carbonate

Magnesium oxide

Milky limewater indicates carbon dioxide is present

Testing for Ammonia

Ammonia turns moist universal indicator paper blue. This happens because ammonia is an alkaline gas.

Red litmus paper can also be used to test for ammonia. If moistened, it will turn blue if ammonia gas is present.

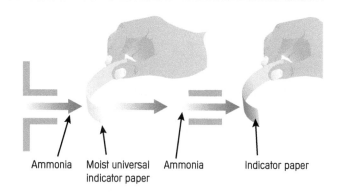

Ammonia

Moist universal indicator paper

Ammonia

Indicator paper

Testing for Chlorine

Chlorine turns moist blue litmus paper red and then bleaches it.

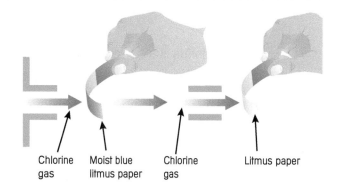

Chlorine gas

Moist blue litmus paper

Chlorine gas

Litmus paper

Quick Test

1. What colour will potassium chloride turn a flame in a flame test? *lilac*
2. A compound is heated with sodium hydroxide solution. A gas is evolved that turns damp red litmus paper blue. Which ion is present in the compound? *ammonia*
3. What is observed when sodium hydroxide solution is added to a solution containing Fe^{2+} ions? *Green precipitate*
4. How can the presence of a carbonate ion (CO_3^{2-}) be determined in a compound?
5. What is observed when silver nitrate solution is added to a solution containing chloride ions?
6. What is the chemical test for the sulfate ion (SO_4^{2-})?
7. What is the test for ammonia gas?
8. Which gas bleaches moist litmus paper?

Exam Practice Questions

1 The Group 1 elements (the alkali metals) react with water.

a) Describe what you would see when a small piece of lithium is added to a large beaker of water. **[2]**

Lithium floats and becomes smaller and bubbles of h₂ given off.

b) Sodium is below lithium in the Periodic Table. Is the reaction of sodium with water more or less vigorous than lithium? **[1]**

P2 c) Explain your answer to **b)**. **[2]**

2 Chlorine is in Group 7 of the Periodic Table. It reacts with hydrogen to form hydrogen chloride.

a) Describe the appearance of chlorine at room temperature. **[2]**

pale green gas.

b) Hydrogen chloride gas is soluble in water. What is the common laboratory name of the solution formed when hydrogen chloride dissolves in water? **[1]**

hydrochloric acid

c) Hydrogen chloride is also soluble in methylbenzene. A student was investigating the properties of hydrogen chloride dissolved in water compared with hydrogen chloride dissolved in methylbenzene.

What did the student observe when universal indicator was added to the two solutions of hydrogen chloride? Explain these observations. **[4]**

d) A student added an aqueous solution of sodium iodide to a solution of bromine. The colour turned from orange to a deep brown.

The student then added an aqueous solution of sodium chloride to a solution of bromine. The orange colour was unchanged.

Explain these observations. [3]

e) The ionic equation for the second reaction in **d)** is shown below.

$$Cl_2 + 2Br^- \longrightarrow 2Cl^- + Br_2$$

With reference to the above equation, explain why it can be described as a redox reaction. [2]

Bromine is oxidised and Chlorine is reduced.

3 The labels have come off four bottles containing colourless solutions of chemicals. The labels are:

- ammonium carbonate solution, $(NH_4)_2CO_3$
- ammonium sulfate solution, $(NH_4)_2SO_4$
- sodium carbonate solution, Na_2CO_3
- sodium sulfate solution, Na_2SO_4

a) Describe how you could test to show the presence of the sulfate ion (SO_4^{2-}). State what would be observed. [2]

b) Describe how you could test to show the presence of the carbonate ion (CO_3^{2-}). State what would be observed. [3]

c) Describe how you could test to show the presence of the ammonium ion (NH_4^+). State what would be observed. **[3]**

d) Describe how you could test to show the presence of the sodium ion (Na^+). State what would be observed. **[2]**

4 A student investigated the reaction of air with copper. $100cm^3$ of air was passed continuously over heated copper using the apparatus below. When the volume remained constant, the apparatus was left to cool and the volume of gas was measured.

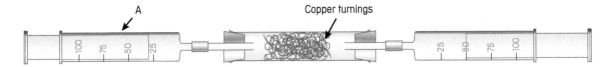

A   Copper turnings

a) What name is given to the piece of apparatus labelled 'A'? **[1]**

b) Indicate on the diagram, with an arrow, where heat should be applied. **[1]**

c) During the experiment, what colour would you expect the copper to turn? **[1]**

d) Why was the apparatus left to cool before measuring the final volume of gas? **[2]**

e) What will be the volume of gas remaining at the end of the experiment? **[1]**

f) Explain your answer to **e)**. **[2]**

5 A student was investigating the conditions needed for rusting to occur. The following test tubes were set up and left for four weeks. Calcium chloride absorbs water.

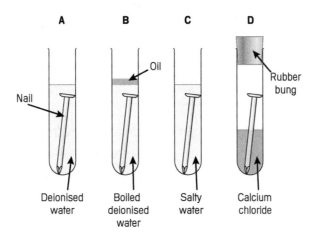

a) What is the purpose of the oil in test tube B? **[1]**

To prevent air reacting + getting into test tube

b) At the end of the experiment, two nails were exhibiting signs of rusting. In which two test tubes were these nails? **[1]**

c) Explain your answer to **b)**. **[2]**

d) What conditions are needed to maximise the amount of rusting? **[1]**

Water + oxygen

e) Name one method of preventing rusting. **[1]**

galvanising

Alkanes

Organic Chemistry

Organic chemistry is the study of covalently bonded compounds containing the element **carbon**. The simplest family of organic molecules are the alkanes.

They form a **homologous series** which means the members have similar chemical properties and their physical properties will show a gradual change.

Hydrocarbons

Hydrocarbons are organic compounds that contain **only** carbon and hydrogen:
- Carbon atoms can make four bonds each.
- Hydrogen atoms can make one bond each.

To make a hydrocarbon, hydrogen atoms react with carbon atoms to form **covalent** bonds. When this happens, carbon atoms share a pair of electrons with hydrogen atoms to make a covalent bond.

Alkanes

The **alkanes** are a group of **hydrocarbons**. In an alkane the carbon atoms are joined together by single carbon–carbon bonds.

Alkanes contain only single bonds, so they are **saturated** hydrocarbons. The general formula for an alkane is C_nH_{2n+2}, where n is the number of carbon atoms.

The table below shows the molecular and displayed formulae for the first five members of the alkane series. They show a gradual change in physical properties, such as the boiling point increasing as the chain length increases.

Many alkanes are obtained from the fractional distillation of crude oil.

Alkane	Molecular Formula	Displayed Formula	Boiling Point (°C)	State at Room Temperature and Pressure
Methane	CH_4	H–C–H (with H above and below)	−162	Gas
Ethane	C_2H_6	H–C–C–H (with H above and below)	−89	Gas
Propane	C_3H_8	H–C–C–C–H (with H above and below)	−42	Gas
Butane	C_4H_{10}	H–C–C–C–C–H (with H above and below)	0	Gas
Pentane	C_5H_{12}	H–C–C–C–C–C–H (with H above and below)	36	Liquid

Key Words   Hydrocarbon • Alkanes • Saturated

Combustion of Alkanes

Alkanes are commonly used as fuels. Methane, the simplest alkane, is the major component of natural gas, a fossil fuel.

When fuels react with oxygen (in air), they burn and release useful heat energy. This is called **combustion**, and it needs a plentiful supply of oxygen (air).

Complete combustion of an alkane, e.g. methane, in air produces carbon dioxide and water.

methane + oxygen $\longrightarrow$ carbon dioxide + water
$CH_4(g) + 2O_2(g) \longrightarrow CO_2(g) + 2H_2O(l)$

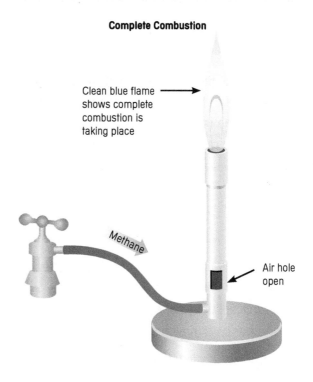

Complete Combustion

Clean blue flame shows complete combustion is taking place

Air hole open

Methane

Incomplete Combustion of Alkanes

When fuels burn without enough oxygen, then **incomplete combustion** happens. Some heat energy is released, but not as much as complete combustion.

Incomplete combustion of a hydrocarbon produces carbon monoxide (a poisonous gas). This is why gas appliances should be serviced regularly.

methane + oxygen $\longrightarrow$ carbon monoxide + water
$2CH_4(g) + 3O_2(g) \longrightarrow 2CO(g) + 4H_2O(l)$

When very little oxygen is present, incomplete combustion of a hydrocarbon produces carbon (soot) and water.

methane + oxygen $\longrightarrow$ carbon + water
$CH_4(g) + O_2(g) \longrightarrow C(s) + 2H_2O(l)$

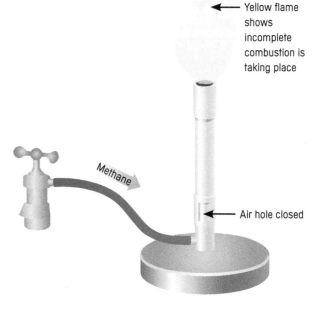

Incomplete Combustion

The yellow flame makes lots of soot

Yellow flame shows incomplete combustion is taking place

Air hole closed

Methane

Alkanes

Reaction of Methane with Bromine

Alkanes are useful fuels but apart from during combustion, they are fairly unreactive.

In the presence of ultraviolet (UV) light, methane will react with bromine. The UV light is needed to supply energy to start the reaction. In this reaction, a hydrogen atom is replaced with a bromine atom and such reactions are referred to as **substitution reactions**.

This reaction shows the formation of bromomethane:

methane **+** bromine ➡ bromomethane **+** hydrogen bromide

$$CH_4(g) + Br_2(g) \rightarrow CH_3Br(g) + HBr(g)$$

Isomerism

The carbon atoms in alkanes do not always arrange themselves in straight chains. As carbon atoms form four covalent bonds, they can form bonds with up to four other carbon atoms.

The two structures below both have the molecular formula C_4H_{10} but the carbon atoms are arranged in different ways.

Butane

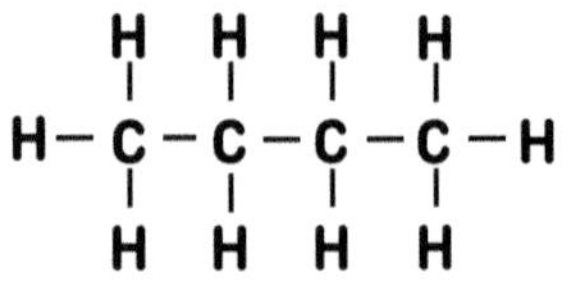

Methylpropane

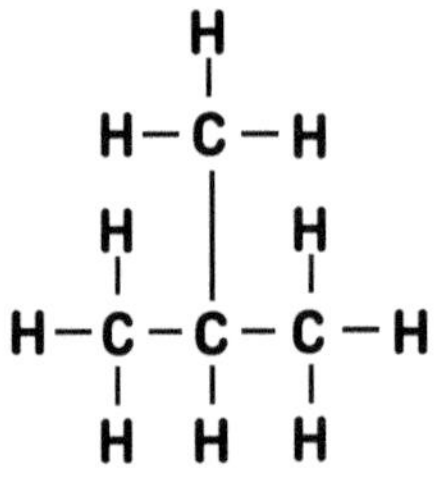

These are known as **isomers** – they have the same molecular formula but different structures. Methylpropane is an isomer of butane. The arrangement of the carbon atoms affects the physical properties of the alkane.

Longer alkanes have more isomers. The alkane C_5H_{12} has three isomers as shown in the following table.

Isomer	Displayed Formula
Pentane	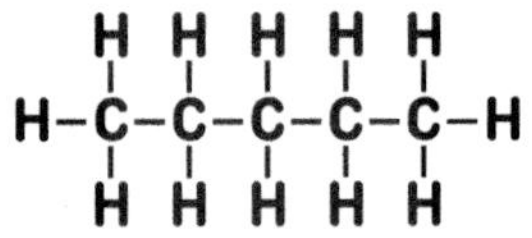 H-C-C-C-C-C-H
2-methylbutane	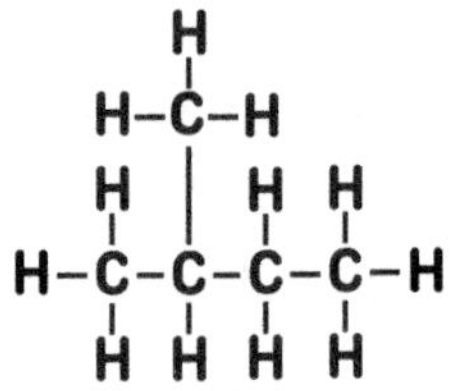 H-C-C-C-C-H
2,2-dimethylpropane	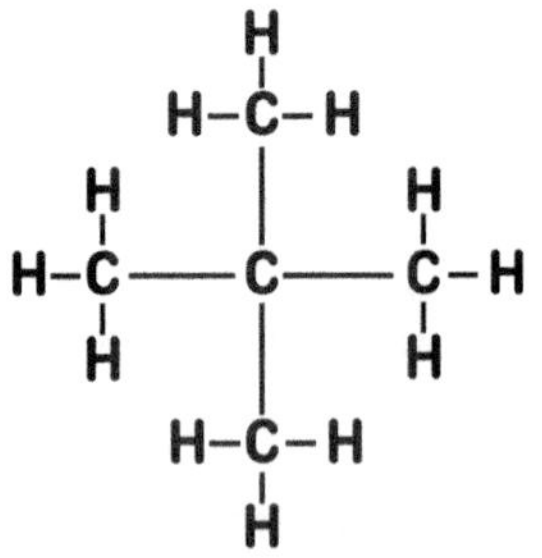 H-C—C—C-H

Quick Test

1. What are hydrocarbons?
2. What are the products of the complete combustion of alkanes?
3. What two products are formed if methane reacts with a small amount of bromine?
4. What are isomers?

About Alkenes

When a hydrocarbon chain has **one or more double carbon–carbon** (C=C) **covalent bonds**, it's called an **alkene**.

Double bonds have two shared pairs of electrons. The name of an alkene always ends in **-ene**.

The general formula for alkenes is C_nH_{2n}.

Alkenes have at least one double covalent bond, so the carbon atom isn't bonded to the maximum number of hydrogen atoms. Alkenes are described as being **unsaturated**.

Alkenes form another homologous series with similar chemical and physical properties. Like alkanes, alkenes burn in air. However, they are much more reactive than alkanes because of the carbon–carbon double bond. Alkenes are obtained from the **cracking** of larger hydrocarbons (see page 89) and are used to make **polymers**.

For example:
- ethene is used to make polyethene
- propene is used to make polypropene.

This table shows the molecular formula, displayed formula and some physical properties of the first three alkenes. The physical properties change gradually as the carbon chain length increases.

Alkene	Molecular Formula	Displayed Formula	Boiling Point (°C)	State at Room Temperature and Pressure
Ethene	C_2H_4		−104	Gas
Propene	C_3H_6		−48	Gas
But-1-ene	C_4H_8		−6	Gas

Alkenes

Testing for Alkenes

A simple test to distinguish between alkenes and alkanes is to add bromine water:

- Alkenes **decolourise** bromine water. (The unsaturated alkene reacts with it.)
- Alkanes have no effect on bromine water, i.e. the bromine water stays orange. (The saturated alkane can't react with it.)

This reaction is a test for unsaturation. It is an **addition reaction** between bromine water and the C=C to make a colourless dibromo compound.

The Reaction of Ethene and Bromine

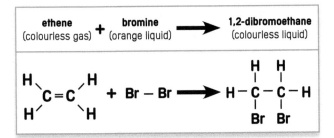

In this reaction the double bond breaks and a bromine atom is added to each carbon atom.

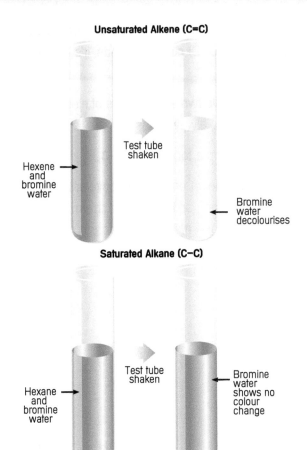

Isomers

Like alkanes, alkenes can also form isomers. The carbon–carbon double bond can be located in different positions.

The different isomers of butene, C_4H_8, are shown below.

But-1-ene   But-2-ene

The number in the name of each isomer indicates the location of the double bond, e.g. but-2-ene means the double bond is between the second and third carbon atoms.

There is another isomer of C_4H_8 whose structure is shown below. It's called methylpropene, but you won't be expected to name it in an exam.

Quick Test

1. What is the general formula for alkenes?
2. What is the chemical test and observation for unsaturated hydrocarbons?
3. What type of reaction occurs when ethene reacts with bromine?
4. Draw the displayed formula of propene.

P2 Ethanol and Alcohols

Alcohols are a family of organic compounds containing hydrogen, carbon and oxygen. Ethanol (C_2H_5OH) is an alcohol. Its displayed formula is shown below:

$$H-\underset{\underset{H}{|}}{\overset{\overset{H}{|}}{C}}-\underset{\underset{H}{|}}{\overset{\overset{H}{|}}{C}}-O-H$$

Ethanol has many uses, for example it can be used:

- to make alcoholic drinks
- to make solvents, such as methylated spirits
- as fuel for cars.

P2 Making Ethanol by Fermentation

Ethanol can be made by fermentation. Yeast is used to ferment glucose solution.

glucose $\longrightarrow$ ethanol + carbon dioxide
$C_6H_{12}O_6 \longrightarrow 2C_2H_5OH + 2CO_2$

The apparatus used in fermentation prevents air (oxygen) from reaching the fermentation mixture.

The fermentation mixture has to be kept at about 30°C for a few days. This is the **optimum temperature** for the enzymes in the yeast to change the glucose into ethanol. This is a renewable method.

Pure ethanol can be extracted from the fermentation mixture by **distillation**.

The absence of air from fermentation prevents the formation of ethanoic acid by oxidation of the ethanol.

The temperature of the fermentation mixture has to be kept at approximately 30°C (the optimum temperature) because:

- if it falls below the optimum temperature, the yeast becomes inactive
- if it rises above the optimum temperature, the enzymes in the yeast start to denature and stop working.

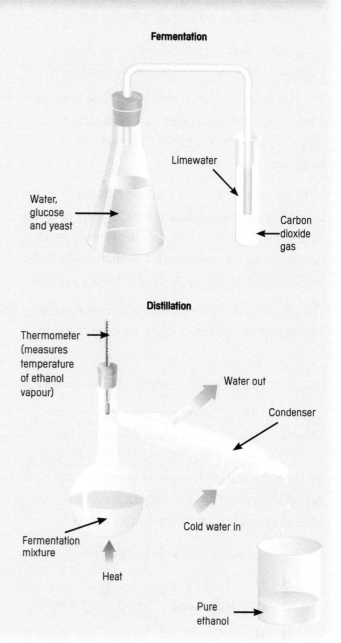

Fermentation

Water, glucose and yeast

Limewater

Carbon dioxide gas

Distillation

Thermometer (measures temperature of ethanol vapour)

Water out

Condenser

Cold water in

Fermentation mixture

Heat

Pure ethanol

Ethanol Production

P2 Making Ethanol by Hydration

The chemical reaction to turn ethene into ethanol is **reversible**:

ethene **+** steam $\xrightleftharpoons[\text{Dehydration}]{\text{Hydration}}$ ethanol

ethene **+** steam $\underset{\text{(Catalyst)}}{\overset{\substack{\text{phosphoric}\\\text{acid}}}{\rightleftharpoons}}$ ethanol
$C_2H_4 + H_2O \rightleftharpoons C_2H_5OH$

Ethene can be **hydrated** to make ethanol by passing it over a heated phosphoric acid catalyst with steam.

Ethanol made in this way is for industrial use only and the method is non-renewable.

In addition to a phosphoric acid catalyst, a temperature of 300°C and a pressure of about 60–70 atmospheres are used. Any unreacted reactants are recycled and fed through the system again.

P2 Fermentation or Hydration?

The two methods of making ethanol have different advantages and disadvantages. These need to be considered before a company chooses which method to use.

Different countries will use different methods depending on the availability of sugar cane or crude oil. Ethene is available in large quantities in the UK due to cracking in oil refineries. Countries like Brazil use fermentation, as sugar cane is readily available.

The ethanol made by hydration is non-renewable because ethene will have been made by cracking

components of crude oil. It is quicker to produce ethanol by hydration, which is a continuous process.

Ethanol made by fermentation is renewable and more sustainable.

Making ethanol by hydration produces less waste products. But fermentation has a higher percentage yield as the reaction is not reversible.

Fermentation is a slow batch process and the ethanol has to be purified by distillation before use. This uses a lot of energy and is expensive.

P2 Dehydration of Ethanol

As shown above, the industrial process to make ethanol is a reversible reaction. Given the right conditions, ethanol can be changed back to ethene by removing water. This type of reaction is called a **dehydration reaction**. The ethanol is vaporised and passed over a hot aluminium oxide catalyst.

ethanol $\longrightarrow$ ethene **+** water
$H-\underset{\underset{H}{\vert}}{\overset{\overset{H}{\vert}}{C}}-\underset{\underset{H}{\vert}}{\overset{\overset{H}{\vert}}{C}}-OH(g) \longrightarrow \overset{H}{\underset{H}{}}C=C\overset{H}{\underset{H}{}}(g) + H_2O(g)$

Quick Test

1. Give two uses of ethanol.
2. What conditions are needed for fermentation to occur?
3. Which catalyst is used in the conversion of ethene to ethanol?
4. How is the ethanol produced by fermentation purified?
5. Ethanol can be dehydrated to make ethene. What catalyst is used in this reaction?

1. Methane and ethane are the first two members of the homologous series of alkanes. Their structures are shown below.

Methane, CH_4

```
        H
        |
    H − C − H
        |
        H
```

Ethane, C_2H_6

```
      H   H
      |   |
  H − C − C − H
      |   |
      H   H
```

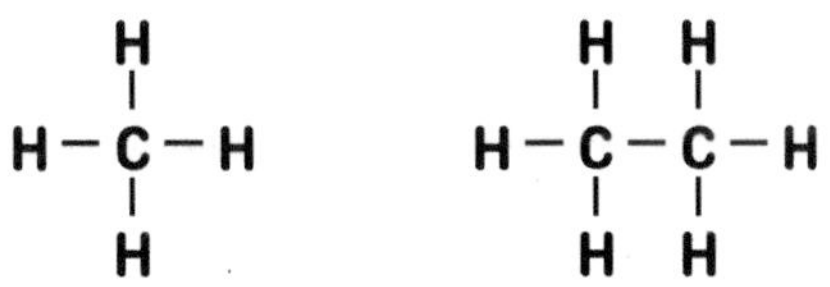

a) What is meant by the term **homologous series**? [2]

   They have similar chemical and~~t~~ their physical properties. Show a gradual change

b) Alkanes are **saturated hydrocarbons**. Explain the meaning of the two terms in bold.

   Saturated: *means that alkanes only contain single* [1] *bonds*

   Hydrocarbon: *are organic compounds that contain* [1] *carbon and hydrogen*

c) Propane is the next member of the alkane series. Draw the structure of propane in the space below. [1]

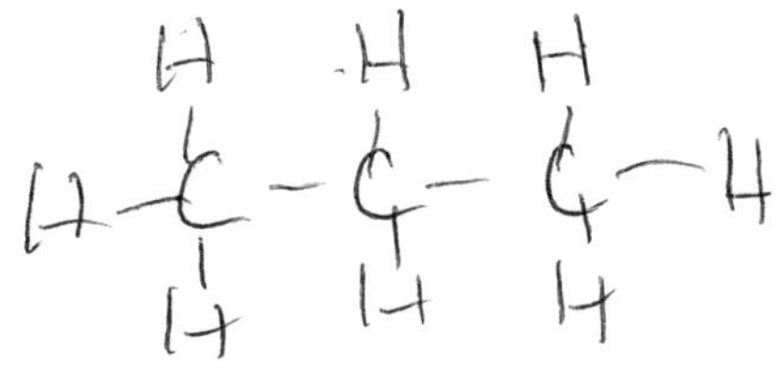

```
    H   H   H
    |   |   |
H − C − C − C − H
    |   |   |
    H   H   H
```

d) Methane is the major constituent of natural gas. What are the products of the complete combustion of methane? [2]

   carbon dioxide and water

e) Write a balanced symbol equation for the complete combustion of methane. [2]

   $$CH_4(g) + 2O_2(g) \rightarrow CO_2(g) + 2H_2O(l)$$

   $\begin{array}{r} 47 \\ \times 2 \\ \hline 94 \end{array}$

f) An alkane is discovered that contains 47 carbon atoms. How many hydrogen atoms will be present in a molecule of this hydrocarbon? [1]

   $H = 2 \times 47 + 2$ C_nH_{2n+2}

   96 $2 \times 2 + 2$

g) Methane reacts with a small amount of bromine. What condition is necessary for this reaction to occur? [1]

   It should react in the presence of UV

h) What is the name of the organic product formed from the reaction in **g)**? [1]

   bromomethane

Exam Practice Questions

2 Consider the two molecules below:

Molecule A   Methylpropene

a) What is the molecular formula of these molecules? **[1]**

....

b) What is the general formula of the homologous series to which both of these molecules belong? **[1]**

....

c) Draw the structure of the first member of this homologous series. **[1]**

d) What is the name of molecule A? .... **[1]**

e) Molecule A and methylpropene are isomers of each other. What do you understand by the term **isomers**? **[2]**

....

....

f) A student has a test tube of a gas which he wishes to test to see if it is an alkene. Describe the test and observed result that would confirm that the gas is an alkene. **[2]**

....

....

(P2) **3** Ethanol (C_2H_5OH) can be manufactured from sugars such as glucose.

a) Draw the molecular structure of ethanol. **[1]**

b) What is the name of the process that produces ethanol from sugars? **[1]**

....

c) Yeast and water are also added to the sugar. What is the purpose of the yeast? **[1]**

....

P2 d) In this reaction a temperature of approximately 30°C is typically used. Explain the disadvantages of using a lower or higher temperature than this. **[3]**

e) In this reaction glucose ($C_6H_{12}O_6$) is converted to ethanol and carbon dioxide (CO_2). Write a balanced symbol equation for this reaction. **[1]**

Ethanol can also be manufactured by the direct reaction between ethene (C_2H_4) and steam.

f) Write a balanced symbol equation for this reaction. **[1]**

g) Name the catalyst used in this process. **[1]**

h) Apart from a catalyst, what other conditions are needed in this reaction? **[2]**

4 Ethanol can be manufactured either by fermentation or by the reaction of ethene with steam. Explain and evaluate the factors that should be considered when deciding which method of manufacture is appropriate. **[6]**

5 Ethanol can be converted into ethene in the reaction shown below.

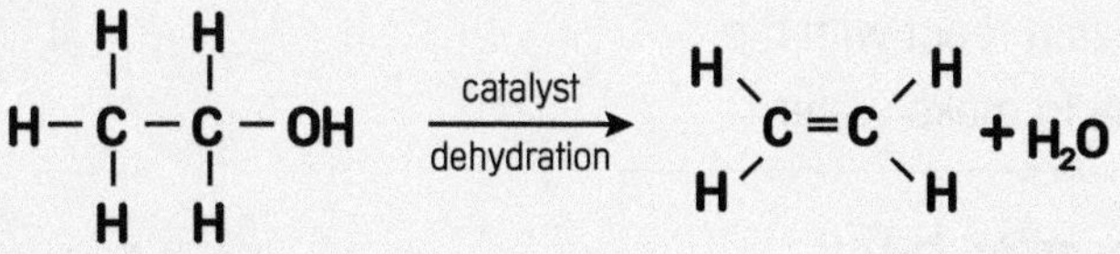

a) Which catalyst is used in this reaction? **[1]**

b) What type of reaction is this? **[1]**

Acids, Alkalis and Salts

Indicators and the pH Scale

Indicators are useful dyes that become different colours in **acids** and **alkalis**.

The table below shows the colours that **indicators** turn when they are in acidic and alkaline solutions.

Indicator	Colour in Acid	Colour in Alkali
Litmus	Red	Blue
Phenolphthalein	Colourless	Pink
Methyl orange	Pink	Yellow

Single indicators, such as litmus or phenolphthalein, produce a sudden, sharp colour change during titration, which clearly shows the **end point** (the point at which **neutralisation** occurs).

The **pH scale** is a measure of the acidity or alkalinity of an **aqueous solution** across a 14-point scale:

- **Acids** are substances that have a pH less than 7.
- Bases are the oxides and hydroxides of metals. Soluble bases are called **alkalis** and have a pH greater than 7.

Universal indicator is a mixture of different indicators, which gives a continuous range of colours. The pH of a solution can be determined by comparing the colour of the indicator in solution to a pH colour chart.

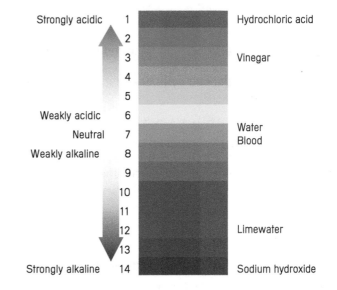

Neutralisation

Acidic compounds produce aqueous **hydrogen ions**, $H^+(aq)$, when they dissolve in water.

Alkaline compounds produce aqueous **hydroxide ions**, $OH^-(aq)$, when they dissolve in water.

When you mix together an **acid** and an **alkali** in the correct amounts, they 'cancel out' each other. This type of reaction is called **neutralisation**.

$$acid + base \longrightarrow salt + water$$

The **hydrogen ions** from the **acid** react with the **hydroxide ions** from the **alkali** to make water:

$$H^+(aq) + OH^-(aq) \longrightarrow H_2O(l)$$

For example, hydrochloric acid and potassium hydroxide can be neutralised:

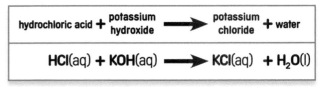

$$hydrochloric\ acid + potassium\ hydroxide \longrightarrow potassium\ chloride + water$$

$$HCl(aq) + KOH(aq) \longrightarrow KCl(aq) + H_2O(l)$$

Neutralising Hydrochloric Acid (HCl) and Potassium Hydroxide (KOH)

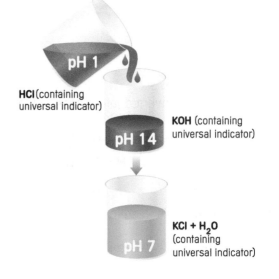

HCl (containing universal indicator)

KOH (containing universal indicator)

KCl + H$_2$O (containing universal indicator)

Naming Salts

The **first name** of a salt comes from the name of the **base or carbonate** used. For example:

- **sodium** hydroxide will make a **sodium** salt
- **copper** oxide will make a **copper** salt
- **calcium** carbonate will make a **calcium** salt
- **ammonia** will make an **ammonium** salt.

The **second name** of the salt comes from the **acid** used. For example:

- hydro**chlor**ic acid will produce a **chlor**ide salt
- **sulf**uric acid will produce a **sulf**ate salt
- **nitr**ic acid will produce a **nitr**ate salt
- **phosph**oric acid will produce a **phosph**ate salt.

For instance, neutralising **potassium** hydroxide with **nitric** acid will produce **potassium nitrate**.

Making Salts

Salts can be either soluble or insoluble. The majority of salts are soluble.

Here are the general rules for predicting whether a salt will be soluble:

- All common sodium, potassium and ammonium salts are soluble.
- All common nitrates are soluble.
- All common chlorides, except silver chloride, are soluble.
- All common sulfates, except barium and calcium, are soluble.
- All common carbonates are insoluble, except potassium, sodium and ammonium.

Soluble salts can be made using a range of methods.

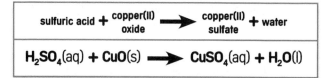

acid **+** base ⟶ salt **+** water

sulfuric acid **+** copper(II) oxide ⟶ copper(II) sulfate **+** water

$$H_2SO_4(aq) + CuO(s) \longrightarrow CuSO_4(aq) + H_2O(l)$$

acid **+** carbonate ⟶ salt **+** water **+** carbon dioxide

hydrochloric acid **+** calcium carbonate ⟶ calcium chloride **+** water **+** carbon dioxide

$$2HCl(aq) + CaCO_3(s) \longrightarrow CaCl_2(aq) + H_2O(l) + CO_2(g)$$

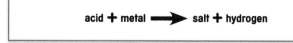

acid **+** metal ⟶ salt **+** hydrogen

hydrochloric acid **+** magnesium ⟶ magnesium chloride **+** hydrogen

$$2HCl(aq) + Mg(s) \longrightarrow MgCl_2(aq) + H_2(g)$$

acid **+** alkali ⟶ salt **+** water

nitric acid **+** sodium hydroxide ⟶ sodium nitrate **+** water

$$HNO_3(aq) + NaOH(aq) \longrightarrow NaNO_3(aq) + H_2O(l)$$

Quick Test

1. What colour is methyl orange indicator in an acid?
2. Which ion do all acids contain?
3. What is the name of the salt formed when magnesium oxide reacts with nitric acid?
4. Which one of the following salts is insoluble?
   a) Ammonium carbonate
   b) Barium sulfate
   c) Copper(II) nitrate
5. What are the products of the reaction between copper(II) carbonate and sulfuric acid?

Acids, Alkalis and Salts

Making Soluble Salts

To make a salt (e.g. potassium nitrate), follow these steps. Make sure you can identify the apparatus.

1. Measure out the alkali (e.g. potassium hydroxide) into a basin using a measuring cylinder. Add the acid (e.g. nitric acid) from a burette.
2. Use a glass rod to put a drop of solution onto indicator paper to test the pH. Continue to add the acid a bit at a time until the solution is neutral (pH 7).
3. Evaporate the solution slowly until crystals form on the end of a cold glass rod placed in the solution. Leave to cool and crystallise.
4. Filter to separate the crystals from the solution.
5. Remove the crystals, wash them and leave to dry.

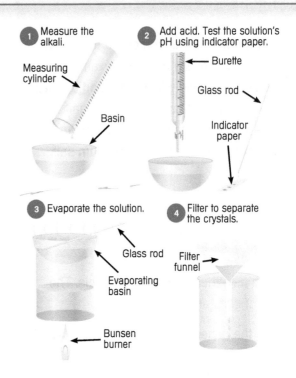

1. Measure the alkali.

Measuring cylinder

Basin

2. Add acid. Test the solution's pH using indicator paper.

Burette

Glass rod

Indicator paper

3. Evaporate the solution.

Glass rod

Evaporating basin

Bunsen burner

4. Filter to separate the crystals.

Filter funnel

Making Insoluble Salts

Insoluble salts can be made from **precipitation reactions**. Calcium sulfate and magnesium carbonate are examples of insoluble salts prepared using the method described below.

A **precipitation** reaction occurs when an **insoluble** solid is made by mixing two ionic solutions together. The **precipitate** (the product) is made when ions from one solution collide and react with ions from the other solution.

The following method can be used to make an insoluble compound:

1. Mix the reactant solutions.
2. Filter off the precipitate.
3. Wash the residue in the filter funnel with a little distilled water.
4. Dry the residue (the product) in an oven at 50°C.

2

Filter paper

3

Distilled water

Acid–alkali Titrations

A **titration** is an accurate technique that you can use to find out **how much** of an **acid** is needed to **neutralise** an alkali of known concentration (called a standard solution).

When **neutralisation** takes place, the hydrogen ions (H^+) from the acid join with the hydroxide ions (OH^-) from the alkali to form water (neutral pH).

hydrogen ion **+** hydroxide ion $\longrightarrow$ water molecule
$H^+(aq) + OH^-(aq) \longrightarrow H_2O(l)$

Use this titration method:

1. Wash and rinse a pipette with the alkali that you will use.
2. Use the pipette to measure out a known and accurate volume of the alkali.
3. Place the alkali in a clean, dry conical flask. Add a few drops of a suitable indicator, e.g. phenolphthalein.
4. Place the acid in a burette that has been carefully washed and rinsed with the acid. Take a reading of the volume of acid in the burette (initial reading). Ensure the jet space is filled with acid.
5. Carefully add the acid to the alkali (with swirling of the flask) until the indicator changes colour to show neutrality. This is called the **end point**. Take a reading of the volume of acid in the burette (final reading).
6. Calculate the volume of acid added (i.e. subtract the initial reading from the final reading).

This method can be repeated to check results and can then be performed without an indicator in order to obtain the salt.

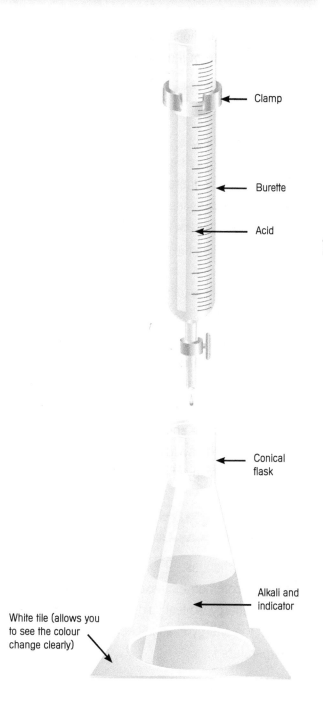

Clamp

Burette

Acid

Conical flask

Alkali and indicator

White tile (allows you to see the colour change clearly)

Quick Test

1. Which method is used to prepare insoluble salts?
2. Name the technique used to accurately neutralise an acid.
3. Write an ionic equation to represent a neutralisation reaction.
4. What is meant by the 'end point' in a titration?

Energetics

Chemical Reactions

When chemical reactions occur, **energy** is transferred **to** or **from** the **surroundings**.

Many chemical reactions are, therefore, accompanied by a **temperature change**.

Exothermic Reactions

Exothermic changes:

- release energy, as heat, and you can detect this energy because there is a temperature rise
- release energy because the **products** have less energy than the **reactants** did.

Common examples of exothermic reactions include:

- combustion
- neutralising acids with alkalis
- hand warmers.

The energy change in an exothermic reaction can be shown using an **energy-level diagram**. Energy is lost to the surroundings, so the products have **less energy** than the reactants.

The arrow shows the energy change or enthalpy change and has the symbol ΔH. In exothermic reactions the enthalpy change has a negative value.

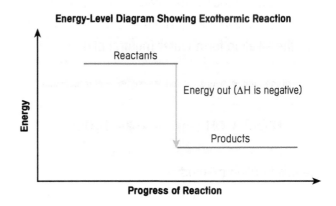

Energy-Level Diagram Showing Exothermic Reaction

Reactants

Energy out (ΔH is negative)

Products

Energy

Progress of Reaction

Endothermic Reactions

Endothermic changes:

- are less common than exothermic changes
- take in energy, so feel cold to the touch. You can detect the energy change because the temperature falls.

Thermal decomposition is an example of an endothermic reaction. Some sports injury packs are based on endothermic reactions.

The energy change in an endothermic reaction can be shown using an **energy-level diagram**. Energy is taken in from the surroundings during the reaction, so the products have **more energy** than the reactants.

In endothermic reactions the enthalpy change, ΔH, is positive.

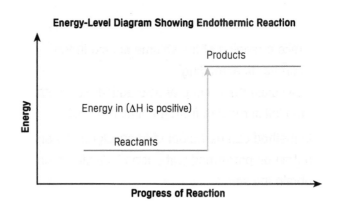

Energy-Level Diagram Showing Endothermic Reaction

Products

Energy in (ΔH is positive)

Reactants

Energy

Progress of Reaction

Key Words   Exothermic • Product • Reactant • Endothermic

Measuring Energy Changes in a Reaction

Energy changes for reactions like neutralisation or displacement can be measured by using a beaker or a polystyrene cup as a **calorimeter**. If a polystyrene cup and a lid is used, very little energy escapes.

By measuring the starting temperature and the maximum temperature rise, the energy released can be calculated using the following equation:

Energy transferred to solution (J)	=	Mass of the solution (g)	×	Specific heat capacity of water (4.2 J/°C)	×	Change in temperature (°C)

Energy change = m × SHC × ΔT

The two experiments below show how the calorimeter would be set up. The reaction on the right is an endothermic reaction, so in this example the maximum temperature drop would be recorded.

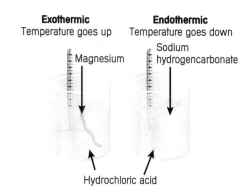

Exothermic
Temperature goes up
Magnesium

Endothermic
Temperature goes down
Sodium hydrogencarbonate

Hydrochloric acid

Comparing Fuels

A **calorimeter** can be used to compare the amounts of heat energy released by the combustion of different fuels. This is a **calorimetry** experiment.

If you burn the same mass of each fuel, the fuel that produces the largest temperature rise releases the most energy per gram of fuel.

To make your calorimetry reliable, you should repeat your experiment and take an average (mean) of the temperature rise. To help you compare fuels, you need to calculate the energy released per gram of fuel. To do this you would need to measure the mass of the spirit burner before and after the experiment.

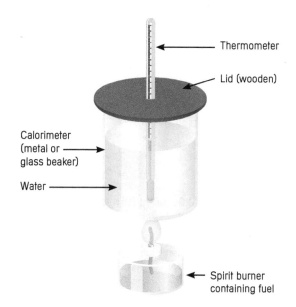

Thermometer

Lid (wooden)

Calorimeter (metal or glass beaker)

Water

Spirit burner containing fuel

Quick Test

1. Which one of the following reactions is not an example of an exothermic reaction?
   a) Neutralisation   **b)** Thermal decomposition   **c)** Combustion
2. Draw and label an energy-level diagram for an endothermic reaction.
3. In a calorimetry experiment, 50g of water is heated up by 10°C. What is the energy change? The specific heat capacity of water is 4.2 J/g/°C.
4. In a calorimetry experiment comparing the amount of energy released by different fuels, why is it important to have the burner and calorimeter the same distance apart for each experiment?

Energetics

Calculating Energy Changes

To compare fuels, you need to work out the amount of energy transferred by the fuel to the water in the **calorimetry** experiment.

Energy transferred (J)	=	Mass of water heated (g)	×	Specific heat capacity of water (J/g/°C)	×	Change in temperature (°C)

$$Q = M \times C \times \Delta T$$

N.B. Specific heat capacity is a constant that is specific to a particular material. Water has a value of 4.2J/g/°C.

Example

The results from a calorimetry experiment with hexane are as follows:
- Mass of hexane burned = 0.26g
- Rise in temperature of water = 12°C
- Mass of water in calorimeter = 200g

Calculate the energy transferred.

= 200g × 4.2J/g/°C × 12°C = **10 080 joules**

P2 Calculating the Molar Enthalpy Change

To calculate the enthalpy (energy) change for 1 mole of a fuel (the **molar enthalpy change**), you first need to work out the energy transferred per gram.

$$\text{Energy per gram} = \frac{\text{Energy supplied (J)}}{\text{Mass of fuel burned (g)}}$$

For example:

$$\text{Energy per gram of hexane} = \frac{10\,080\text{J}}{0.26\text{g}}$$

$$= 38\,769\text{J/g}$$

$$= 38.8\text{kJ/g}$$

From this value, you can work out the molar enthalpy change using:

Molar enthalpy change	=	Energy transferred per gram (kJ)	×	Molar mass of fuel

N.B. 1kJ = 1000J

Example

Calculate the molar enthalpy of hexane fuel.

$$\text{Molar mass of hexane, } C_6H_{14} = (6 \times 12) + (14 \times 1) = 86\text{g}$$

$$\text{Molar enthalpy change for hexane} = 38.8 \times 86$$

$$= \textbf{3336.8kJ/mol}$$

N.B. The actual value for hexane is 4163kJ/mol. Our result is less because some energy is lost to the surroundings and some to the calorimeter.

Making and Breaking Bonds

In a chemical reaction, the bonds in the reactants must be broken and new bonds made to form the products. The **activation energy** is the energy needed to break bonds to start a reaction. In a chemical reaction:

- **breaking** bonds is an **endothermic** process
- **making** bonds is an **exothermic** process.

Chemical reactions that absorb more energy to break the bonds in the reactants than is released when new bonds are made in the products are **endothermic**.

Chemical reactions in which more energy is released when new bonds are made than was absorbed to break the old bonds are **exothermic**.

P2 Energy Calculations

Example 1

Hydrogen is burned in oxygen to produce water:

hydrogen + oxygen ➡ water

$2H_2(g) + O_2(g)$ ➡ $2H_2O(g)$

$2H-H + O=O$ ➡ $2H-O-H$

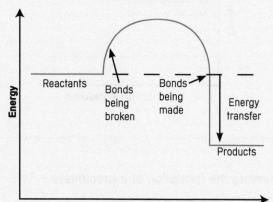

The following are **bond energies** for the **reactants** and **products**:

H–H is 436kJ   O=O is 496kJ   O–H is 463kJ

Calculate the energy change.

You can calculate the energy change using this method:

1 Calculate the energy used to break bonds:
$(2 \times H-H) + O=O = (2 \times 436) + 496$
$= \textbf{1368kJ}$

2 Calculate the energy released when new bonds are made:
(Water is made up of 2 × O–H bonds.)
$2 \times H-O-H = 2 \times (2 \times 463) = \textbf{1852kJ}$

3 Enthalpy change (ΔH) = Energy used to break bonds − Energy released when new bonds are made
$\Delta H = 1368 - 1852$
$\Delta H = \textbf{−484kJ}$

The reaction is **exothermic** because the energy from making the bonds is **more than** the energy needed to break the bonds.

Example 2

Hydrogen and halogens react together to form hydrogen halides. For example, the formation of hydrogen chloride is as follows:

hydrogen + chlorine ➡ hydrogen chloride

$H_2(g) + Cl_2(g)$ ➡ $2HCl(g)$

$H-H + Cl-Cl$ ➡ $2H-Cl$

The following are **bond energies** for the **reactants** and **products**:

H–H is 436kJ   Cl–Cl is 243kJ   H–Cl is 432kJ

Calculate the energy change.

You can calculate the energy change as follows:

1 Calculate the energy used to break bonds:
$H-H + Cl-Cl = 436 + 243 = \textbf{679kJ}$

2 Calculate the energy released when new bonds are made:
$2 \times H-Cl = 2 \times 432 = \textbf{864kJ}$

3 Enthalpy change (ΔH) = Energy used to break bonds − Energy released when new bonds are made
$\Delta H = 679 - 864$
$\Delta H = \textbf{−185kJ}$

The reaction is **exothermic**.

Quick Test

1. During a calorimetry experiment, 6940J of energy was transferred to the calorimeter when 0.29g of ethanol (C_2H_5OH) was burned. What is the molar enthalpy change? Answer in kJ/mol.

2. The energy required to break the bonds in a reaction is 2314kJ. The energy released when the new bonds are made is 3613kJ. What is the enthalpy change for this reaction?

3. Is the reaction in Question 2 exothermic or endothermic?

Rates of Reaction

Factors Affecting Rates of Reaction

Chemical reactions only occur when reacting particles **collide** with each other with **sufficient energy**.

The **minimum amount** of energy required to cause a reaction is called the **activation energy**. Particles must collide with sufficient energy to overcome the activation energy. If the activation energy for a reaction is low, more collisions will be successful and result in a reaction. Reactions with high activation energies have a slower rate of reaction for a certain temperature.

The five important factors that affect the rate of reaction are: **temperature, concentration, pressure, surface area** and use of a **catalyst**.

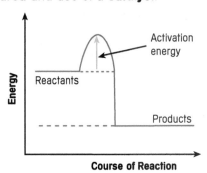

Course of Reaction

Rate of Reaction Experiments

Chemical reactions **stop** when one of the **reactants** is **used up** first.

Often, there is not the same amount of each type of reactant. The limiting reactant is the one that is used up by the end of the reaction.

If there are more reactants there are more reactant particles, so more product particles can be made. The limiting reactant determines the maximum amount of product that can be made.

The rate of a **chemical reaction** is the amount of products made in a given unit of time.

The rate of a chemical reaction can be found in three different ways:

1. Weighing the reaction mixture.
2. Measuring the volume of gas produced.
3. Observing the formation of a precipitate.

Weighing the reaction mixture – If one of the products is a gas, you could weigh the reaction mixture at timed intervals. The mass of the mixture will decrease as the gas is produced and escapes.

Measuring the volume of gas produced – You could use a gas syringe to measure the total volume of gas produced at timed intervals.

Observing the formation of a precipitate – This can be done by:

- watching a cross on a tile underneath the jar to see when it's no longer visible
- monitoring a colour change using a light sensor.

Weighing the Reaction Mixture

Measuring the Volume of Gas Produced

Observing the Formation of a Precipitate

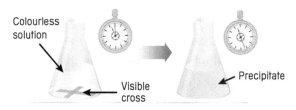

Colourless solution

Visible cross

Precipitate

Analysing the Rate of Reactions

From a graph, you can find out the following:

1 **How long it takes to make the maximum amount of products** by drawing a vertical line down to the *x*-axis (time) from the horizontal line. (The horizontal line on the graph shows that the reaction is finished.)

2 **How much product was made** by drawing a horizontal line from the highest point on the graph across to the *y*-axis.

3 **Which reaction is quicker** by comparing the steepness of the lines.

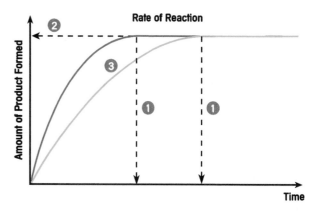

Collision Theory

Collision theory states that for two reactant particles to react, they must collide. But when they collide, they need to have enough energy so that they don't simply bounce off each other. This is called the **activation energy**.

If the reactant particles collide more **frequently**, the reaction will speed up. If the particles collide with more energy, they're more likely to have successful collisions, which will also speed up the reaction.

Temperature

In a reaction at **low temperature**, the particles move slowly. This means that the particles collide less often, and at lower energy, so fewer collisions will be successful. The rate of reaction will be slow.

In a reaction at **high temperature**, the particles move more quickly. This means that particles collide more often, and at higher energy. The rate of reaction will be fast.

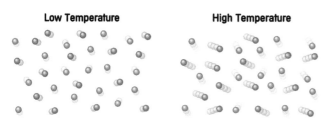

Increasing temperature causes an increase in the **kinetic energy** of the particles, i.e. they move a lot faster.

The faster the particles move, the greater the chance of them colliding, so the number of collisions per second increases:

- **More frequent collisions between particles lead to a faster reaction.**

When the particles collide at an increased temperature, they have more energy. High energy collisions increase the chance of them being successful collisions:

- **More energetic collisions lead to more successful collisions.**

Quick Test

1 State three factors that affect the rate of a reaction.

2 Increasing the temperature of a reaction increases the _____ energy of the particles.

Rates of Reaction

Concentration of the Reactants

In a reaction where one or both reactants are in **low concentrations**, the particles will be spread out. The particles will collide with each other less often, so there will be fewer successful collisions.

If there is a **high concentration** of one or both reactants, the particles will be crowded close together. The particles will collide with each other more often, so there will be many more successful collisions.

Increasing concentration increases the number of particles in the same volume, i.e. the particles are much more crowded together.

The more crowded the particles, the greater the chance of them colliding, which increases the number of collisions per second:

- **More frequent collisions lead to a faster reaction.**

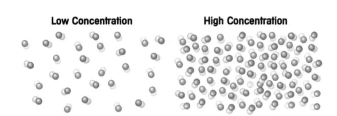

Low Concentration   High Concentration

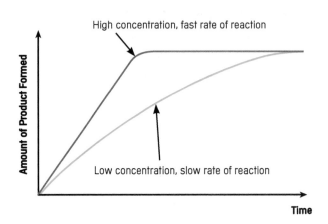

High concentration, fast rate of reaction

Low concentration, slow rate of reaction

Amount of Product Formed

Time

Pressure of a Gas

When a gas is under a **low pressure**, the particles are spread out. The particles will collide with each other less often, so there will be fewer successful collisions (similar to a low concentration of reactants in a solution).

When the **pressure is high**, the particles are crowded more closely together. The particles collide more often, resulting in many more successful collisions (similar to a high concentration of reactants in a solution).

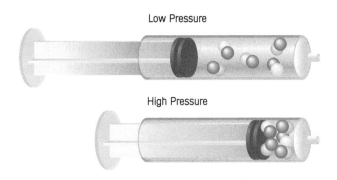

Low Pressure

High Pressure

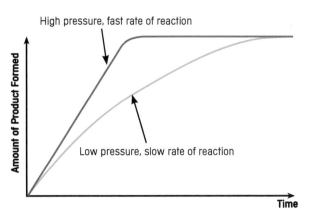

High pressure, fast rate of reaction

Low pressure, slow rate of reaction

Amount of Product Formed

Time

Surface Area

The **larger** the **surface area** of a reactant, the **faster** the reaction. **Powdered solids** have a larger surface area compared to their volume than **lumps of solids**. This means there are **more particles** on the **surface** for the other reactants to collide with.

The greater the number of particles exposed, the greater the chance of them colliding, which **increases** the rate of the **reaction**. So powders can have very fast reactions, much faster than a lump of the same reactant.

A greater proportion of particles exposed in a powdered solid means the particles have a **greater chance** of **colliding**, which means the frequency of collisions increases. (There are more collisions each second.)

An explosion is a very fast reaction where huge volumes of gas are made.

Workers in factories that handle powders, such as flour, custard powder or sulfur, have to be very careful because the **dust** of these materials can **mix** with **air** and could cause an **explosion** if there is a **spark**.

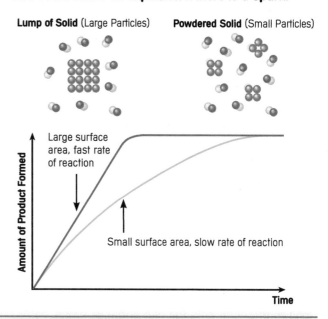

Lump of Solid (Large Particles)   **Powdered Solid** (Small Particles)

Using a Catalyst

A **catalyst** is a substance that **changes** the rate of a chemical **reaction** without being used up or changed at the end of the reaction. Catalysts are often used to speed up the rate of reaction.

Catalysts are very useful materials, as only a **small amount** of catalyst is needed to speed up the reaction of large amounts of reactant.

You can see how a catalyst affects the rate of reaction by looking at the graph. This graph shows two reactions that eventually produce the same amount of product. One reaction takes place much faster than the other because a catalyst is used.

Catalysts speed up the rate of reaction by lowering the activation energy of the reaction. They provide an alternative reaction pathway. This means more particles have enough energy to collide and successfully react.

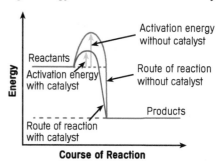

Course of Reaction

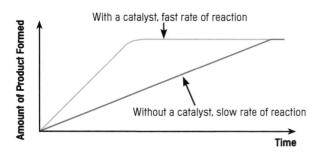

Quick Test ~~Porm~~ ~~has a larger~~ ~~surface are some more~~ ~~collisions occur with wid~~ ~~& more~~ ~~particles~~

1 Why does the same mass of powdered magnesium react much more vigorously with acid than magnesium ribbon does?

2 How do catalysts increase the rate of a reaction? ~~catalysts are a substance that changes the rate of reaction without being used up or changed in the end~~

Equilibria

Reversible Reactions

Some chemical reactions are **reversible**. In a **reversible reaction**, the **products** can react together to produce the original **reactants**. We represent this with a special double-headed arrow: $\rightleftharpoons$

$$A + B \rightleftharpoons C + D$$

This means that:

- A and B can react together to produce C and D
- C and D can react together to produce A and B.

For example, the decomposition of ammonium chloride is a reversible reaction:

ammonium chloride $\rightleftharpoons$	ammonia **+** hydrogen chloride
$NH_4Cl(s) \rightleftharpoons$	$NH_3(g)$ **+** $HCl(g)$

Solid ammonium chloride decomposes when heated to produce ammonia and hydrogen chloride gas (both colourless).

Ammonia reacts with hydrogen chloride gas to produce clouds of white ammonium chloride powder.

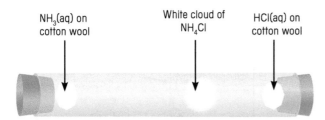

Another example involves hydrated copper(II) sulfate crystals. They change from blue crystals to a white powder when heated and water is released as steam. The addition of water then reverses this change.

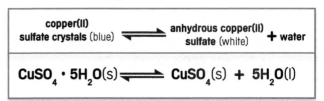

copper(II) sulfate crystals (blue) $\rightleftharpoons$ anhydrous copper(II) sulfate (white) **+** water

$$CuSO_4 \cdot 5H_2O(s) \rightleftharpoons CuSO_4(s) + 5H_2O(l)$$

Adding Water to Anhydrous Copper(II) Sulfate

Dynamic Equilibrium

A reversible reaction will reach a state of **dynamic equilibrium** if it is in a closed system and left for long enough.

At equilibrium, the concentrations of reactants and products don't change over time. The relative amounts of all the reacting substances at equilibrium depend on the conditions of the reaction.

When a dynamic equilibrium is established, the forward and backward reactions happen at exactly the same rate, which explains why the concentration of products (and reactants) doesn't change over time.

Changing the Position of Equilibrium

Once a reversible reaction has reached equilibrium, it is possible to change the equilibrium position (or yield) by changing the temperature or pressure. The yield is the amount of product made.

Adding a catalyst has no effect on the equilibrium position. It would speed up both the forward and reverse reaction at the same rate.

The Effect of Changing Temperature

In an **exothermic** reaction:
- if the temperature is **raised**, the **yield decreases**
- if the temperature is **lowered**, the yield **increases**.

In an **endothermic** reaction:
- if the temperature is **raised**, the **yield increases**
- if the temperature is **lowered**, the yield **decreases**.

Consider the following reaction:

$$H_2(g) + Cl_2(g) \rightleftharpoons 2HCl(g) \qquad \Delta H = -ve$$

The forward reaction is exothermic (because ΔH is negative). This means that if the temperature is raised then the yield decreases, i.e. the equilibrium position moves to the left-hand side.

The Effect of Changing Pressure

In **gaseous reactions**, an increase in pressure favours the reaction that produces the least number of molecules.

Consider the following reaction:

$$N_2(g) + 3H_2(g) \rightleftharpoons 2NH_3(g)$$

There are four molecules of gas on the left-hand side and two on the right-hand side. If the pressure is increased then the yield of ammonia (NH_3) increases because higher pressure favours the reaction that produces fewer molecules, i.e. the equilibrium position moves to the right-hand side.

Quick Test

Dynamic equilibrium

$$\rightarrow NH_4Cl(s) \rightleftharpoons NH_3(g) + HCl(g)$$

1. What does the symbol $\rightleftharpoons$ represent in an equation? _A reversible reaction_
2. Solid ammonium chloride (NH_4Cl) decomposes to form hydrogen chloride (HCl) gas and ammonia (NH_3) gas. This reaction is reversible. Write a symbol equation for this reaction.
3. What state does a reversible reaction reach if it is in a closed system and is left for long enough?
4. In a reversible reaction, what happens to the equilibrium position if the forward reaction is endothermic and the temperature is increased? _The yield increases equilibrium moves to right hand side_
5. In the equation below, what is the effect on the yield of C when the pressure is increased? _The yield increases_
   $2A(g) + B(g) \rightleftharpoons C(g)$

Exam Practice Questions

1 A student was performing a titration to determine the concentration of a solution of hydrochloric acid. She set up the apparatus as shown.

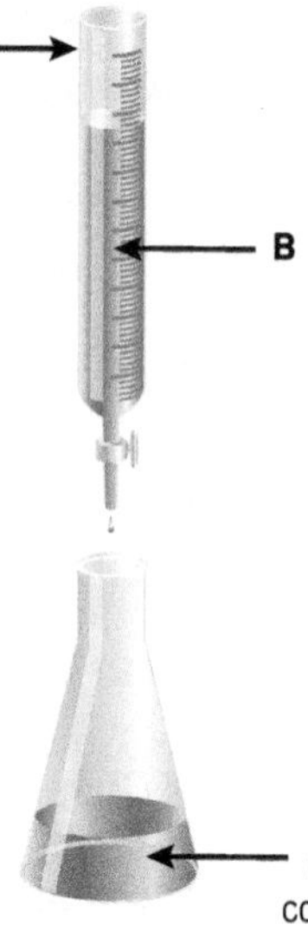

A ⟶

B

Acid of unknown concentration

a) Name the piece of apparatus labelled 'A'. **[1]**

burette

b) Suggest the name of a suitable chemical for label 'B'. **[1]**

alkali

c) Chemical 'B' must be of a known concentration. What name is given to a solution whose exact concentration is known? **[1]**

Standard solution

d) A few drops of an indicator were added to the acid at the beginning of the experiment. Give the name of a suitable indicator and state what colour you would expect it to be at the start and end of the experiment. **[3]**

e) Which ion is present in all acids? *H^+ (Hydrogen)* **[1]**

f) Explain why the student should repeat the titration. **[1]**

2 Copper(II) sulfate is a soluble salt. It can be prepared by the reaction of dilute sulfuric acid with a suitable base such as copper(II) carbonate.

a) Write a word equation for the reaction of sulfuric acid with copper(II) carbonate. **[1]**

Copper (II) Sulfate + carbonate → copper carbonate + H_2O + CO_2

b) Plan an experiment to obtain a sample of solid copper(II) sulfate by this reaction. You may include a diagram in your answer and you should include details of the method and any apparatus used. **[5]**

c) Barium sulfate is an insoluble salt. Name two solutions that can be mixed together to form barium sulfate. **[2]**

d) After the two solutions in **c)** have been mixed, how can pure barium sulfate be separated from the remaining solution? **[1]**

e) What type of reaction is taking place in this reaction? **[1]**

precipitation

3 A student was carrying out an experiment into the energy changes associated with the neutralisation of sodium hydroxide by hydrochloric acid.

25cm³ of sodium hydroxide was placed into a polystyrene (coffee) cup and the temperature recorded, as shown in the diagram. 25cm³ of hydrochloric acid, at the same temperature, was added, the mixture stirred with the thermometer and the final temperature recorded.

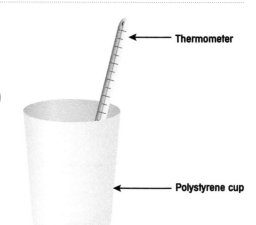

Thermometer

Polystyrene cup

a) Why was a polystyrene cup used in this experiment instead of a glass beaker? **[1]**

It's a good insulator.

b) The initial temperature was 18.5°C and the final temperature was 32.8°C. Calculate the temperature change during this reaction. **[1]**

The energy-level diagram for this reaction is shown below.

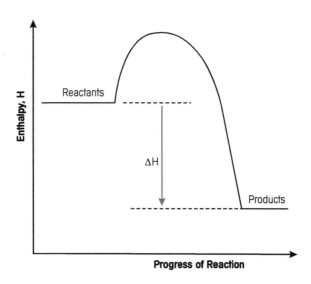

Exam Practice Questions

c) What does ΔH represent? **[1]**

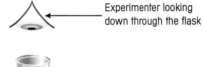 Enthal

d) In this experiment is the value of ΔH positive or negative? Explain your answer. **[2]**

4 A pupil was investigating the effect of temperature on the rate of reaction between aqueous sodium thiosulfate with dilute hydrochloric acid. When the acid is added to the sodium thiosulfate solution, a precipitate of sulfur gradually forms. The pupil recorded the time taken for a cross written on a piece of paper to disappear from view.

The experiment was repeated at different temperatures. The results are shown in the table below.

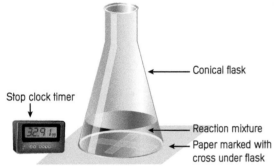

Temperature (°C)	Time taken for cross to disappear from view (s)
15	70
25	44
40	30
55	22
70	14

a) On the grid below, plot a graph of the time taken against temperature. Connect your points with a smooth curve. **[2]**

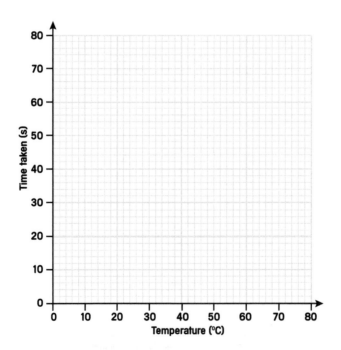

b) At which temperature was the reaction the fastest? [1]

....

c) Describe how the temperature affects the rate of the reaction. Explain your answer in terms of collisions. [2]

....

....

d) Suggest how the rate of this reaction at 30°C will change when the concentration of hydrochloric acid is increased. Explain your answer. [2]

....

....

5 Consider the reaction below.

$2SO_2(g) + O_2(g) \rightleftharpoons 2SO_3(g)$

a) What does the $\rightleftharpoons$ symbol represent? [1]

The symbol represents reversible reaction

b) What would be the effect on the yield of SO_3 if the above reaction was carried out at a higher pressure? Explain your answer. [3]

....

....

....

c) The forward reaction is exothermic. What would be the effect on the yield of SO_3 if the above reaction was carried out at a higher temperature? Explain your answer. [3]

....

....

....

Extraction and Uses of Metals

Properties of Metals

A metal is chosen for a particular purpose because of the **properties** that it has. For example, the table shows the properties of aluminium and iron.

Property	Aluminium	Iron
Dense	✗	✓
Magnetic	✗	✓
Resists corrosion	✓	✗
Malleable	✓	✓
Conducts electricity	✓	✓
Strong	✗	✓
Ductile	✓	✓

Due to their properties, iron and aluminium can both be used to build cars. Both metals can be pressed into shape (they are malleable) and they are both good electrical conductors.

In addition:
- **Aluminium** does not rust or corrode and it is less dense than iron (making a lighter car with a better fuel economy).
- **Iron** is cheaper and stronger than aluminium and is also magnetic, so it can be separated for recycling more easily.

Many cars are also made from **steel**. Steel is an alloy of iron and carbon. Steel has different properties from iron which make it more useful, e.g. it is harder and does not corrode as fast as iron.

Iron and steel have many uses including bridges, railway lines, food cans and paper clips.

Aluminium is also used to make airplanes, cooking foil and drinks cans. Aluminium can be mixed with other metals, such as copper and magnesium, to improve its strength.

Extracting Metals

The very unreactive metals, such as gold and silver, can be found in the Earth's crust as uncombined metals and just have to be dug out. Most metals are more reactive and are found combined with other elements such as oxygen. Rocks rich in these metal compounds are called **ores**.

The Reactivity Series

A metal's position in the reactivity series can be used to determine what method has to be used to extract it from its ore. The more reactive the metal is, the harder it is to extract.

The position of carbon is important. Carbon (or carbon monoxide) can be used as a reducing agent and will react with metal oxides to remove the oxygen and release the metal. Metals above carbon in the series are too reactive to be extracted by heating with carbon. They are usually extracted by electrolysis of the molten ore.

Metal	Method of Extraction	Reactivity
Potassium	Electrolysis	
Sodium		
Lithium		
Calcium		
Magnesium		
Aluminium		
(Carbon)		
Zinc	Heating with carbon or carbon monoxide	
Iron		
Copper		
Silver	Found as uncombined metals	
Gold		

Extraction and Uses of Metals

Extracting Aluminium

Aluminium is the most abundant metal in the Earth's crust. It must be obtained from its ore by electrolysis because it is too reactive to be extracted by heating with carbon. The electrodes are made of graphite (a type of carbon). The aluminium ore (bauxite) is purified to leave aluminium oxide, which is then melted so that the ions can move.

When a current passes through the molten mixture:
* positively charged aluminium ions move towards the negative electrode (cathode) and form aluminium
* negatively charged oxygen ions move towards the positive electrode (anode) and form oxygen.

The positive electrodes gradually wear away (because the graphite electrodes react with the oxygen to form carbon dioxide gas). This means they have to be replaced every so often. Extracting aluminium can be quite an expensive process because of the cost of the large amounts of electrical energy needed to carry it out.

The electrolysis of aluminium can be represented by the following equation:

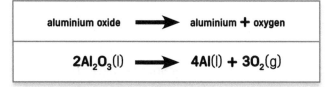

aluminium oxide $\longrightarrow$ aluminium + oxygen
$2Al_2O_3(l) \longrightarrow 4Al(l) + 3O_2(g)$

In the extraction of aluminium, the aluminium oxide is mixed with cryolite (a compound of aluminium), which acts as a solvent to lower its melting point. This reduces the operating temperature and the energy needed for the process.

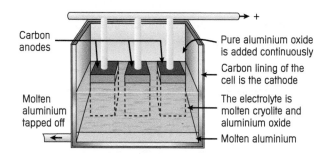

Carbon anodes — Pure aluminium oxide is added continuously — Carbon lining of the cell is the cathode — The electrolyte is molten cryolite and aluminium oxide — Molten aluminium — Molten aluminium tapped off

The electrolysis of molten aluminium oxide can be represented by the following two half-equations.

At the cathode:

$$Al^{3+} + 3e^- \xrightarrow{\text{Reduction}} Al$$

At the anode:

$$2O^{2-} \xrightarrow{\text{Oxidation}} O_2 + 4e^-$$

Extracting Iron from Iron Ore

Over a billion tonnes of iron are produced worldwide every year. It is our most widely used metal.

The iron is extracted from iron ore in a blast furnace, which gets its name from the blast of hot air that is blown in the bottom of the furnace. The other two raw materials are coke and limestone, and along with the iron ore they are fed into the top of the furnace.

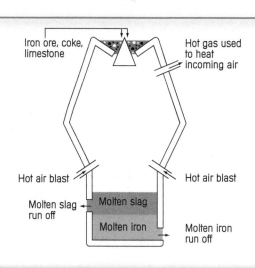

Iron ore, coke, limestone — Hot gas used to heat incoming air — Hot air blast — Hot air blast — Molten slag run off — Molten slag — Molten iron — Molten iron run off

Extraction and Uses of Metals

Extracting Iron from Iron Ore (Cont.)

Coke

Coke is made by heating coal in a large oven in the absence of air so it does not burn. It breaks down into coke, a form of carbon. In the blast furnace the coke burns in the oxygen in the air blasted in from the bottom. This heats up the furnace and makes carbon dioxide gas.

carbon + oxygen $\longrightarrow$ carbon dioxide
$C + O_2 \longrightarrow CO_2$

Some of the carbon dioxide made reacts with more coke to make carbon monoxide.

carbon dioxide + carbon $\longrightarrow$ carbon monoxide
$CO_2 + C \longrightarrow 2CO$

Carbon monoxide acts as a reducing agent in the furnace.

Iron Ore

One type of iron ore is called haematite. It contains iron(III) oxide (Fe_2O_3). This must be reacted with a reducing agent that will remove the oxygen to extract the iron. Carbon monoxide is a strong enough reducing agent to convert iron(III) oxide to iron.

iron(III) oxide + carbon monoxide $\longrightarrow$ iron + carbon dioxide
$Fe_2O_3 + 3CO \longrightarrow 2Fe + 3CO_2$

The furnace is so hot that the iron forms as a liquid and because it is dense it falls down and collects at the bottom of the furnace. The molten iron is run off into waiting containers and is taken away to be made into steel.

Limestone

Limestone is added to remove all the rocky impurities that were in the iron ore (mostly silicon dioxide). Limestone is calcium carbonate ($CaCO_3$) and it decomposes in the heat of the furnace to make calcium oxide (CaO) and carbon dioxide (CO_2).

calcium carbonate $\longrightarrow$ calcium oxide + carbon dioxide
$CaCO_3 \longrightarrow CaO + CO_2$

The calcium oxide then combines with the silicon dioxide impurities to make calcium silicate.

calcium oxide + silicon dioxide $\longrightarrow$ calcium silicate
$CaO + SiO_2 \longrightarrow CaSiO_3$

Calcium silicate is known as **slag**. It forms a liquid and falls to the bottom of the furnace. It is less dense than iron and floats on top. It is run off and cooled so it forms a solid. It is sold to be made into building materials and road surfaces.

Quick Test

1. State one advantage that aluminium has over iron in the manufacture of cars.
2. What method is used to extract the following metals from their ores?
   a) Aluminium
   b) Iron
3. In the extraction of aluminium, why is cryolite added to the aluminium oxide?
4. What are the three raw materials used in the blast furnace?
5. What is the slag produced in the blast furnace used for?

Fractional Distillation

Crude oil is a mixture of many **hydrocarbons**. A hydrocarbon is a molecule that contains only **carbon** and **hydrogen** atoms. Different hydrocarbons have different boiling points. This means crude oil can be separated into useful products or **fractions** (parts) by **heating** it in a process called **fractional distillation**.

As you go up the column, the fractions have a lower boiling point and become less viscous (more runny).

Forces Between Molecules

In hydrocarbons there are:

- strong covalent bonds between the atoms in the molecule
- weak **intermolecular** forces (forces of attraction between molecules).

The intermolecular forces between longer hydrocarbons are stronger than the forces between shorter hydrocarbons. When a liquid hydrocarbon is boiled, its molecules move faster and with more energy until all the intermolecular forces are broken and it becomes a gas.

COLD
The fractions with low boiling points rise to the top of the column

Short-chain hydrocarbon

Fractions with different boiling points condense at different levels of the column and can be collected

Long-chain hydrocarbon

The fractions with high boiling points condense and are collected at the bottom of the column

Crude oil vapour

HOT

Refinery gases – e.g. propane and butane for bottled gases

70°C **Gasoline (petrol)** – fuel for cars

180°C **Kerosene (paraffin)** – fuel for jet aircraft

260°C **Diesel oil (gas oil)** – fuel for cars and large vehicles

Fuel oil – fuel for heating systems and some power stations

340°C

Over 400°C **Bitumen** – to make roads

Small molecules have very weak forces of attraction between them, which are easy to overcome by heating. It's the differences in their boiling points which allow us to separate a mixture of hydrocarbons (e.g. crude oil) by the process of **fractional distillation**.

Cracking

The composition of crude oil is such that, when it is fractionally distilled, there are not enough small-chained hydrocarbons to meet the demand for products such as gasoline and there are far too many long-chained hydrocarbons.

To use up the unwanted long-chained hydrocarbon molecules, they are broken down into the more useful short-chained hydrocarbons (alkanes and alkenes).

This industrial process is called cracking and it needs a catalyst (alumina or silica), a high temperature (600–700°C) and a high pressure. Cracking can be done in the laboratory, as shown in the diagram.

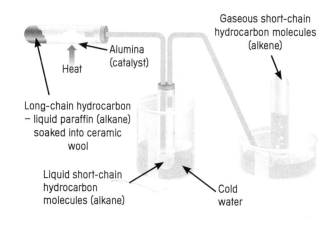

Gaseous short-chain hydrocarbon molecules (alkene)

Alumina (catalyst)

Heat

Long-chain hydrocarbon – liquid paraffin (alkane) soaked into ceramic wool

Liquid short-chain hydrocarbon molecules (alkane)

Cold water

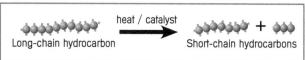

Long-chain hydrocarbon → heat / catalyst → Short-chain hydrocarbons

Crude Oil

Incomplete Combustion

If a fuel burns without sufficient oxygen, e.g. in a car engine when cold or when a gas appliance needs servicing, then **incomplete combustion** takes place and **carbon monoxide** (a poisonous gas) can be formed. The equation shows the incomplete combustion of methane.

Carbon monoxide is poisonous because it binds with red blood cells and this stops oxygen being carried in the bloodstream.

methane	+	oxygen	→	carbon monoxide	+	water
$2CH_4$	+	$3O_2$	→	$2CO$	+	$4H_2O$

Formation of NO$_x$ Gases

During the combustion of fuels, high temperatures (e.g. in a car engine) can cause **nitrogen** in the atmosphere to **react** with **oxygen**. This produces **nitrogen monoxide (NO)**:

nitrogen	+	oxygen	→	nitrogen monoxide
$N_2(g)$	+	$O_2(g)$	→	$2NO(g)$

Nitrogen monoxide is then **oxidised** to produce **nitrogen dioxide (NO$_2$)**:

nitrogen monoxide	+	oxygen	→	nitrogen dioxide
$2NO(g)$	+	$O_2(g)$	→	$2NO_2(g)$

When NO and NO_2 occur together, they're called **NO$_x$**.

In
- Air – mostly nitrogen and oxygen.
- Hydrocarbon fuel such as petrol or diesel.

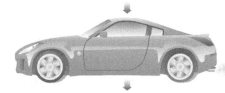

Out
- The normal products of combustion.
- **Carbon monoxide** – poisonous gas made when the fuel does not burn completely.
- **Oxides of nitrogen** – formed inside the internal combustion engine.

Acid Rain

Some fossil fuels, such as crude oil fractions and coal, contain sulfur compounds as impurities.

When coal or oils are burned, the sulfur impurities produce sulfur dioxide. Sulfur dioxide and nitrogen dioxide dissolve in water to produce acid rain.

Acid rain can:
- erode stonework and corrode metals
- make rivers and lakes acidic and kill aquatic life
- kill plants.

Quick Test

1. How are the different fractions in crude oil separated?
2. Why is cracking an important process?
3. What conditions are used in the industrial cracking of hydrocarbons?
4. How are NO$_x$ gases formed?
5. State two problems caused by acid rain.

Addition Polymerisation

The alkenes made by cracking are small molecules which can be used as **monomers**. The double bonds in alkenes are easily broken, so monomers can be joined together to make **polymers** (large, long-chained molecules). Plastics are polymers.

When the alkenes join together making a polymer, the reaction is called **addition polymerisation**. This process needs **high pressure** and a **catalyst**.

You could use displayed formulae to show a polymerisation reaction, for example ethene monomers making poly(ethene):

Ethene monomers (unsaturated)

$$H \quad H \quad\quad H \quad H$$
$$| \quad | \quad\quad\quad | \quad |$$
$$C = C \; + \; C = C \; +$$
$$| \quad | \quad\quad\quad | \quad |$$
$$H \quad H \quad\quad H \quad H$$

... and many more ...

Poly(ethene) polymers (saturated)

$$H \quad H \quad H \quad H$$
$$| \quad | \quad | \quad |$$
$$-C - C - C - C -$$
$$| \quad | \quad | \quad |$$
$$H \quad H \quad H \quad H$$

... and on and on ...

However, it's better to use the standard way of displaying an addition polymer formula by showing the **repeat unit** of the structure:

$$n \quad C = C \longrightarrow \left[C - C \right]_n$$

Monomer   Repeat unit of polymer

Polymerisation involves the reaction of many unsaturated monomer molecules, i.e. alkenes, to form a saturated polymer. You should be able to construct the displayed formula of:

- an addition **polymer** if you're given the displayed formula of a monomer, e.g. propene monomer to poly(propene) polymer

$$n \quad C = C \longrightarrow \left[C - C \right]_n$$

Monomer   Polymer

- a **monomer** if you're given the displayed formula of an addition polymer, e.g. poly(propene) polymer to propene monomer.

$$\left[C - C \right]_n \longrightarrow n \quad C = C$$

Polymer   Monomer

Uses of Addition Polymers

Addition polymers have many properties that make them useful. They have a wide range of uses. Here are some examples:
- Poly(ethene): plastic bags, cling film, detergent bottles and packaging.
- Poly(propene): carpets, ropes, packaging and plastic banknotes.

Synthetic Polymers

Disposing of Plastics

We produce large amounts of plastic waste (polymers) which can be difficult to dispose of. This is because plastics are very inert and they are not biodegradable (i.e. they will not be broken down by bacteria or decay).

The table shows the disadvantages of the main ways of getting rid of unwanted plastics.

Using Landfill Sites	Burning Polymers	Recycling Polymers
• Most plastics are non-biodegradable. • Wastes valuable resources. • Landfill sites get filled up very quickly, i.e. they waste land.	• Produces air pollution. • Some plastics produce toxic fumes when they are burned, e.g. burning poly(chloroethene) (PVC) produces hydrogen chloride gas. • Wastes valuable resources.	• Different types of plastic need to be recycled separately – sorting plastics into groups can be time-consuming and expensive.

P2 Another Addition Polymer

Poly(chloroethene) is also known as polyvinylchloride or PVC. It is used in rigid form to make window frames, doors and water pipes. It can also be made flexible by the addition of a plasticiser used to make flooring, wellington boots and the soles of shoes.

Poly(chloroethene) is an addition polymer made from chloroethene.

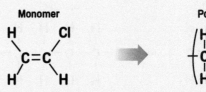

Monomer

Chloroethene (vinyl chloride)

Polymer

Poly(chloroethene)
(Polyvinylchloride or PVC)

P2 Nylon

Nylon is also a very versatile polymer. It has many uses: as a fibre to make clothing, rope and carpets, and in solid form to make hair combs, gear wheels and other mechanical products.

It is made by a different type of polymerisation reaction. It is a condensation polymer.

When the monomers of a condensation polymer react together, with every link a small molecule such as water is made.

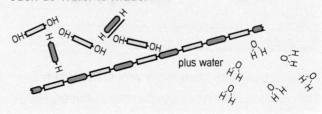

plus water

Quick Test

1. Which conditions are required for addition polymerisation to occur?
2. What is the name of the polymer formed when propene undergoes polymerisation?
3. State two uses of poly(ethene).
4. Give one disadvantage of disposing of polymers using landfill sites.
5. P2 Which method of polymerisation is used to produce nylon?

Ammonia

Ammonia (NH_3) is an alkaline gas made from nitrogen and hydrogen. It can be used to make:
- nitric acid
- **fertilisers** (cheap fertilisers are very important in helping to produce enough food for the growing world population).

The reaction which makes ammonia is a **reversible reaction**. So, nitrogen and hydrogen can form ammonia, and ammonia can decompose to make hydrogen and nitrogen.

Reversible reactions have the symbol ⇌ in their equation to show that the reaction can take place in either direction.

nitrogen + hydrogen ⇌ ammonia
$N_2(g) + 3H_2(g) \rightleftharpoons 2NH_3(g)$

The Haber Process

Ammonia is made on a large scale in the **Haber process**. The reactants are:
- nitrogen (from the air)
- hydrogen (from natural gas or the cracking of hydrocarbons).

Optimum conditions (producing the maximum yield of ammonia) aren't used as they would be very expensive to maintain, so a compromise is reached:
- The nitrogen and hydrogen mixture is under a **high pressure** of 200 atmospheres.
- The gases are passed over an **iron catalyst** at **450°C**.

Only about 15% of the reactant gases make ammonia. The unreacted gases are recycled. Ammonia is cooled, condensed and then pumped off as a liquid.

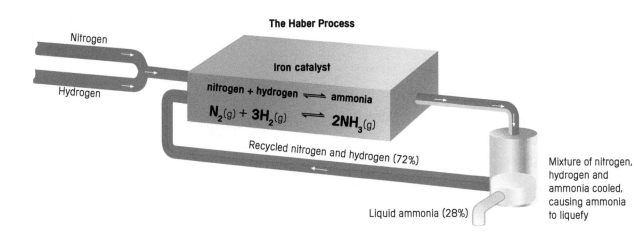

The Haber Process

Manufacturing Chemicals

P2 The Contact Process

The raw materials sulfur, air and water are made into sulfuric acid in the contact process:

1. Sulfur is burned in a furnace to make sulfur dioxide:

sulfur + oxygen $\longrightarrow$ sulfur dioxide
$S(g) + O_2(g) \longrightarrow SO_2(g)$

2. The sulfur dioxide combines with oxygen from the air in a reversible reaction to make sulfur trioxide:

sulfur dioxide + oxygen $\rightleftharpoons$ sulfur trioxide
$2SO_2(g) + O_2(g) \rightleftharpoons 2SO_3(g)$

This reaction takes place using a vanadium(V) oxide (V_2O_5) catalyst, at a temperature of about 450°C and approximately 2 atmospheres pressure.

3. Sulfur trioxide is then dissolved in concentrated sulfuric acid to form oleum ($H_2S_2O_7$).

$SO_3(g) + H_2SO_4(l) \longrightarrow H_2S_2O_7(l)$

The oleum is then diluted with water to the required concentration.

$H_2S_2O_7(l) + H_2O(l) \longrightarrow 2H_2SO_4(aq)$

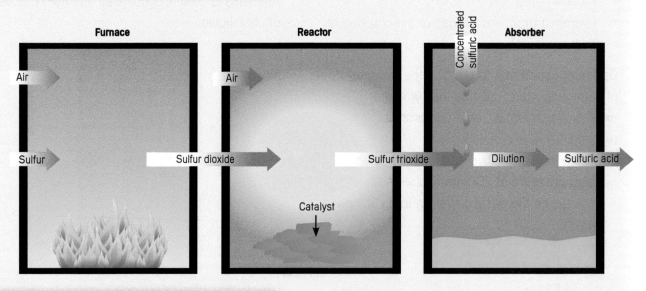

Furnace — Air, Sulfur, Sulfur dioxide
Reactor — Air, Sulfur trioxide, Catalyst
Absorber — Concentrated sulfuric acid, Dilution, Sulfuric acid

P2 Uses of Sulfuric Acid

The sulfuric acid that is produced in the contact process has many uses, such as the manufacturing of:

- paints and pigments
- soaps and detergents
- fibres
- plastics
- fertilisers.

Electrolysis of Sodium Chloride

Sodium chloride (common salt) is a compound of an alkali metal and a halogen. It is found in large quantities in the sea and in underground deposits.

Electrolysis of sodium chloride solution (brine) produces some important reagents for the chemical industry. These are:

- **chlorine gas** (at the positive electrode)
- **hydrogen gas** (at the negative electrode)
- **sodium hydroxide solution** (passed out of the cell).

Chlorine is used to sterilise water supplies and to manufacture hydrochloric acid, disinfectants, bleach and PVC.

Hydrogen is used in the manufacture of ammonia and margarine.

Sodium hydroxide is used in the manufacture of soap, paper and bleach.

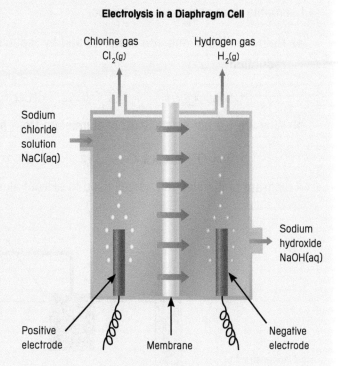

Electrolysis in a Diaphragm Cell

Reactions at the Electrodes

Sodium chloride solution contains the ions Na^+, H^+, Cl^- and OH^-. The H^+ and Cl^- ions are discharged at the electrodes.

Half-equations can be written for the reactions that take place at the electrodes in the electrolysis of concentrated sodium chloride solution.

- Hydrogen is made at the cathode:

$$2H^+ + 2e^- \longrightarrow H_2$$

Electrons are gained – this is reduction.

- Chlorine is made at the anode:

$$2Cl^- \longrightarrow Cl_2 + 2e^-$$

Electrons are lost – this is oxidation.

Sodium ions and hydroxide ions are not discharged and remain to make sodium hydroxide solution.

The electrolysis of sodium chloride is a very important part of the chemical industry. Many other parts of industry depend on the products manufactured by this process.

Quick Test

1. Give two uses of ammonia (NH_3).
2. What temperature and pressure are used in the manufacture of ammonia?
3. P2 What catalyst is used in the contact process?
4. P2 What are the three products of the electrolysis of sodium chloride solution?
5. P2 What is the ionic equation for the reaction that occurs at the cathode in the diaphragm cell?

Exam Practice Questions

1 Aluminium and iron are two useful metals that are extracted from the earth before being made into useful materials. Aluminium is extracted from purified aluminium oxide by electrolysis. Iron is extracted from haematite (iron ore) in a blast furnace.

a) Both aluminium and iron are extracted by reduction. What do you understand by the term **reduction**? [1]

reduction is the gain of electrons

b) Why are we not able to extract aluminium from aluminium oxide in a blast furnace? [1]

Aluminium is more reactive than carbon

A diagram of the electrolysis cell used to extract aluminium is shown below.

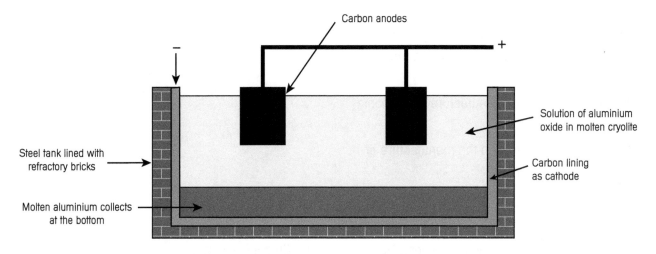

Carbon anodes

Solution of aluminium oxide in molten cryolite

Steel tank lined with refractory bricks

Carbon lining as cathode

Molten aluminium collects at the bottom

c) Why is the aluminium oxide mixed with cryolite? [2]

d) Explain why the anodes need regularly replacing. [2]

e) Other than the purified aluminium oxide and the cryolite, what is the other significant cost in this process? [1]

f) Balance the following ionic half-equation for the reaction occurring at the anode. [2]

$$\_\_O^{2-} \longrightarrow O_2 + \_\_e^-$$

2 Crude oil is separated into its constituent components by fractional distillation. A fractionating column is used to carry out fractional distillation. A diagram of a fractionating column is shown below.

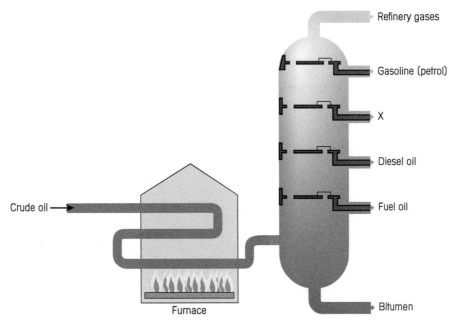

a) What is the name of the fraction labelled as 'X'? **[1]**

Kerosene

b) As you go down the fractionating column, what happens to the boiling point of the fractions? **[1]**

They increase.

Fractional distillation produces more long-chained hydrocarbons than can be used directly. Long-chained hydrocarbons can be converted into shorter-chained hydrocarbons using the apparatus below.

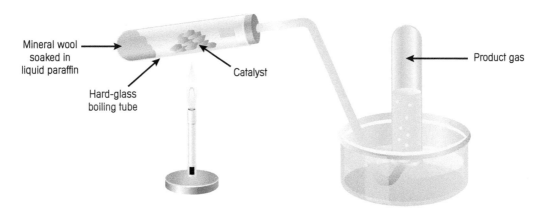

c) What name is given to this process? **[1]**

cracking

d) Suggest a suitable catalyst for this reaction. **[1]**

silica / alumina

Exam Practice Questions

3 Small alkene molecules, such as ethene (C_2H_4), can be made into more useful materials by a process called polymerisation. The structure of ethene is shown below.

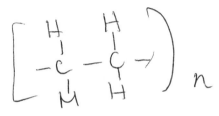

a) What general name is given to the small alkene molecules that undergo polymerisation? **[1]**

monomers

b) Draw the repeat unit for poly(ethene). **[2]**

c) Give two uses for poly(ethene). **[2]**

Plastic bags

d) The disposal of addition polymers causes environmental issues. Explain why addition polymers are hard to dispose of. **[2]**

4 Nitrogen and hydrogen are used in the manufacture of ammonia (NH_3), known as the Haber process. The equation for the reaction is shown below.

$$N_2(g) + 3H_2(g) \rightleftharpoons 2NH_3(g)$$

a) What are the sources of nitrogen and hydrogen for use in the Haber process? **[2]**

b) State the three essential reaction conditions in the Haber process. **[3]**

c) State two uses of ammonia. **[2]**

P2 **5** The electrolysis of concentrated aqueous sodium chloride solution (brine) produces hydrogen, chlorine and sodium hydroxide. The diagram below shows the cell used for this electrolysis.

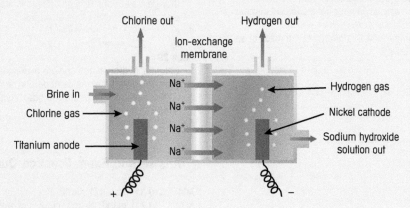

a) State three uses of sodium hydroxide. **[3]**

b) State two uses of chlorine gas. **[2]**

c) Write ionic equations for the reactions that occur at each electrode.

Anode: **[1]**

Cathode: **[1]**

Answers

In the examination, there are three assessment objectives that are tested throughout the exam papers:

AO1 Knowledge and understanding (worth approx. 45–50% of marks in the exam)

AO2 Application of knowledge and understanding, analysis and evaluation (worth approx. 27–33% of marks in the exam)

AO3 Experimental skills, analysis and evaluation of data and methods (worth approx. 20–25% of marks in the exam)

Principles of Chemistry

Answers to Quick Test Questions

Page 5
1. Liquid
2. Gas
3. Boiling and evaporating
4. B

Page 8
1. Diffusion
2. C
3. Fractional distillation
4. Crystallisation

Page 11
1. electrons
2. The total number of protons and neutrons in an atom
3. 11 protons, 11 electrons, 12 neutrons
4. Isotopes are atoms of the same element that have the same number of protons / same atomic number but a different number of neutrons (different mass number).
5. The mass of an atom compared with a twelfth of the mass of an atom of the isotope carbon–12

Page 12
1. a) $(2 \times 7) + 16 = 30$
   b) $(2 \times 14) + [2 \times (4 \times 1)] + 32 + (4 \times 16) = 132$

Page 13
1. $48\,000cm^3$ ($48dm^3$)
2. 0.125 moles

Page 15
1. $4Al + 3O_2 \longrightarrow 2Al_2O_3$
2. 2.18g
3. a) Li_2O
   b) Fe_2O_3

Page 18
1. P_4O_{10}
2. CuO
3. PbO
4. 4.2g

Page 19
1. 77.3%
2. $0.45mol/dm^3$

Page 22
1. X^{3+}
2. Oxidation is loss of electrons.
3. Ca^{2+} and F^-
4. **Any two from:** High melting point; High boiling point; Conduct electricity (when molten or aqueous)
5. The ions in aluminium oxide (Al^{3+} and O^{2-}) have a greater charge than the ions in sodium chloride (Na^+ and Cl^-) and so the attraction between the ions is greater, meaning more energy is required to separate the ions.

Page 24
1. Bonds formed by sharing pairs of electrons between atoms
2. There are weak forces of attraction between the molecules.

3. There are lots of strong covalent bonds that require a lot of energy to break them.

4.

Page 25
1. The electrons are free to move.
2. The layers of metal ions can slide over each other.

Page 27
1. They do not contain free electrons or ions that can move.
2. The ions need to be free to move.
3. The sodium ions are attracted to the negative electrode where they gain electrons. The chloride ions are attracted to the positive electrode where they lose electrons.
4. a) $Al^{3+} + 3e^- \longrightarrow Al$
   b) $2Cl^- \longrightarrow Cl_2 + 2e^-$

Page 29
1. Chlorine, hydrogen and sodium hydroxide
2. Copper is formed at the cathode. Oxygen is formed at the anode.
3. Hydrogen is formed at the cathode. Oxygen is formed at the anode.
4. 0.0622 moles
5. 0.95g

Answers to Exam Practice Questions

AO1 1. a) A = proton **[1 mark]**; B = neutron **[1 mark]**

AO2   b) 7 **[1 mark]**; the total number of protons and neutrons **[1 mark]**

AO1   c) There is 1 electron in the outer shell. **[1 mark]**

AO1   d) Atoms that have the same number of protons **[1 mark]** but different numbers of neutrons **[1 mark]**

AO2   e) $\dfrac{(10 \times 6) + (90 \times 7)}{100} = 6.9$ **[1 mark for the correct numbers on top; 1 mark for having 100 on the bottom; 1 mark for the correct answer (allow error carried forward)]**

AO1   f) A regular arrangement (lattice) of cations **[1 mark]** surrounded by free moving (delocalised) electrons **[1 mark]**. **[Both marks can be gained from a labelled diagram.]**

Make sure that any diagrams are clearly drawn and labelled.

AO2   g) The electrons are able to move / flow through the structure. **[1 mark]**

AO1 2. a) $12 + (2 \times 16) = 44$ **[1 mark]**

AO1   b) 0.25 moles $(\dfrac{3}{12})$ **[1 mark]**

AO2   c) 0.25 moles of C will form 0.25 moles of CO_2. The mass of CO_2 is $0.25 \times 44 = 11g$ **[1 mark for mole calculation; 1 mark for the correct answer]**

AO2 **d)** 1.5×10^{23} $(0.25 \times 6 \times 10^{23})$ **[1 mark]**

AO2 **e)** The volume of 0.25 moles of gas is $0.25 \times 24\ 000$ **[1 mark]** $= 6000cm^3$ / $6dm^3$ **[1 mark for the answer (allowing error carried forward) and the unit]**

In calculation questions, a mark will normally be given for the correct calculation(s), even if the answer is then incorrect. So, it's very important to show all your workings.

AO1 **3.a)** Two or more different elements chemically bonded / joined together **[1 mark]**

AO2 **b)**

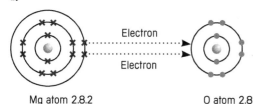

Mg atom 2.8.2   O atom 2.8

[1 mark gained for each arrow]

AO1 **c)** 2+ **[1 mark]**

AO1 **d)** Oxidised **[1 mark]**; electrons are lost **[1 mark]**

AO1 **e)** Strong electrostatic forces of attraction **[1 mark]** between oppositely charged ions (cations and anions) **[1 mark]**

AO1 **f)** Ionic bonds are strong **[1 mark]** and require a lot of energy **[1 mark]** to break them.

Chemistry of the Elements

Answers to Quick Test Questions

Page 35
1. A period
2. Left-hand side (and middle)
3. They have the same number of electrons in the outer shell of their atoms.
4. A non-metal
5. They have full outer shells of electrons and so do not need to react with other elements.

Page 37
1. Sodium hydroxide and hydrogen
2. They become more reactive.
3. The metal floats / moves about the surface / effervesces (produces bubbles of gas).
4. The outer electron in potassium is further away from the nucleus. It is therefore less attracted to the nucleus and so is more easily lost.

Page 40
1. Orange / brown liquid
2. Reactivity decreases as you go down the group.
3. B
4. B
5. The HCl does not split up into ions.

Page 42
1. 20% / 21%
2. Manganese(IV) oxide
3 Sulfur burns with a blue flame.
4. acidic

Page 44
1. Carbon dioxide
2. Thermal decomposition
3. In carbonated (fizzy) drinks and in fire extinguishers
4. Global warming

Page 46
1. Zinc sulfate and hydrogen
2. An explosion and an exothermic reaction

AO2 **g)** The ions in magnesium oxide have a greater charge than the ions in sodium chloride **[1 mark]** and so the electrostatic attraction between them is greater **[1 mark]**.

AO1 **4.a)** The sharing of a pair of electrons between two atoms **[1 mark]**

AO2 **b)**

[1 mark for 3 correct N-H bonds; 1 mark for the pair of electrons in the N shell]

Always double check that you have the correct number of electrons in each shell.

AO1 **c)** There are relatively weak forces **[1 mark]** between the molecules **[1 mark]**.

AO1 **d)** There are lots **[1 mark]** of strong covalent bonds **[1 mark]**.

AO3 **5.a)** The bulb will light. **[1 mark]**

AO1 **b)** There are no ions to carry the charge. It is covalent. **[1 mark]**

AO2 **c)** The ions in solid copper sulfate are not able to move. In solution the ions are free to move and carry the charge. **[1 mark]**

AO2 **d)** Copper is produced at the cathode **[1 mark]** and oxygen is produced at the anode **[1 mark]**.

3. The copper(II) sulfate turns from white to blue.
4. See if the water starts to boil at exactly 100^oC.

Page 49
1. **Any two from:** Potassium; Sodium; Lithium; Calcium; Magnesium
2. Magnesium is more reactive than copper.
3. Copper
4. Magnesium
5. By coating with grease, oil or paint; galvanising

Page 53
1. Lilac
2. The ammonium ion (NH_4^+)
3. A green precipitate (that slowly turns brown)
4. Add acid and pass any gas evolved through limewater. If the limewater turns milky then the compound contains the carbonate ion.
5. A white precipitate
6. Add hydrochloric acid followed by barium chloride solution. A white precipitate will be observed, confirming the presence of the sulfate ion.
7. Ammonia will turn moist universal indicator paper blue and red litmus paper blue.
8. Chlorine

Answers to Exam Practice Questions

AO3 **1. a)** Accept any two of the following points: The metal floats; Effervescence (fizzing and bubbling); The metal moves about the surface of the water; It slowly dissolves. **[2 marks]**.

AO2 **b)** More vigorous **[1 mark]**.

AO1 **c)** Sodium atoms are larger than lithium atoms. The outer electron is therefore further away from the nucleus **[1 mark]**. It is therefore less attracted / less tightly held and so it is more easily lost, meaning sodium is more reactive **[1 mark]**.

AO1 **2.a)** Green / yellow **[1 mark]** gas **[1 mark]**

AO1 **b)** Hydrochloric acid **[1 mark]**

AO2 **c)** No change with the methylbenzene solution **[1 mark]** because the HCl molecules do not dissociate **[1 mark]**. The

Answers

universal indicator will turn red when added to the HCl in water **[1 mark]** because the HCl molecules dissociate **[1 mark]**.

AO3   **d)** Iodide has been converted (oxidised) to iodine **[1 mark]**. The first experiment shows that bromine is more reactive than iodine **[1 mark]**. The second experiment shows that chlorine is more reactive than bromine **[1 mark]**.

AO2   **e)** Chlorine gains electrons – this is reduction **[1 mark]**. Bromide ions lose electrons – this is oxidation **[1 mark]**.

AO3   **3.a)** Add barium chloride solution **[1 mark]**. A white solid / precipitate will form **[1 mark]**.

AO3   **b)** Add an acid, e.g. hydrochloric acid **[1 mark]**. Bubbles of gas (effervescence) will be observed **[1 mark]**, which turn limewater milky **[1 mark]**.

AO3   **c)** Gently warm **[1 mark]** with sodium hydroxide solution **[1 mark]**. A gas is produced that turns moist red litmus paper blue **[1 mark]**.

AO3   **d)** Perform a flame test **[1 mark]**. A yellow flame will be observed **[1 mark]**.

AO3   **4.a)** Gas syringe **[1 mark]**

AO3   **b)** Under the copper turnings **[1 mark]**

AO3   **c)** Black **[1 mark]**

AO2   **d)** Gas expands when heated **[1 mark]**. By allowing it to cool, a true volume can be recorded **[1 mark]**.

AO1   **e)** Approximately 80cm^3 **[1 mark]**

AO2   **f)** Approximately 20% of the air is oxygen **[1 mark]**. It is the oxygen in the air that reacts with the copper in this experiment **[1 mark]**.

AO3   **5.a)** To prevent air / oxygen coming into contact with the water **[1 mark]**

AO3   **b)** A and C **[1 mark]**

AO3   **c)** They were exposed to water **[1 mark]** and air / oxygen **[1 mark]**.

AO1   **d)** Water, air / oxygen and salt **[1 mark]**

AO1   **e)** Galvanising / coating with zinc (or other more reactive metal) or with paint / oil / grease / plastic **[1 mark]**

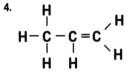

Organic Chemistry

Answers to Quick Test Questions

Page 60

1. Molecules that contain carbon and hydrogen only
2. Carbon dioxide and water
3. Bromomethane and hydrogen bromide
4. Molecules that have the same molecular formula but different structures

Page 62

1. C_nH_{2n}
2. Add bromine water. Bromine water turns from orange/brown to colourless (it is decolourised).
3. Addition reaction
4.

$$H-\overset{\displaystyle H}{\underset{\displaystyle H}{C}}-\overset{\displaystyle H}{\underset{\displaystyle H}{C}}=C\overset{\displaystyle H}{\underset{\displaystyle H}{<}}$$

Page 64

1. **Any two from:** To make alcoholic drinks; To make solvents; As fuel for cars
2. Sugar (glucose) solution, yeast, temperature approx. 30°C, anaerobic conditions
3. (Heated) phosphoric acid
4. Distillation
5. Aluminium oxide

Answers to Exam Practice Questions

AO1   **1. a)** A group of compounds that have the same general formula **[1 mark]** and similar chemical/physical properties **[1 mark]**.

AO1   **b)** Saturated – contain single bonds only **[1 mark]**; Hydrocarbons – molecules that contain carbon and hydrogen only **[1 mark]**

AO1   **c)**

$$H-\overset{\displaystyle H}{\underset{\displaystyle H}{C}}-\overset{\displaystyle H}{\underset{\displaystyle H}{C}}-\overset{\displaystyle H}{\underset{\displaystyle H}{C}}-H$$

[1 mark]

AO1   **d)** Carbon dioxide **[1 mark]** and water **[1 mark]**

AO1   **e)** $CH_4 + 2O_2 \longrightarrow CO_2 + 2H_2O$ **[1 mark for correct formulae; 1 mark for balancing equation]**

AO2   **f)** 96 **[1 mark]**

AO1   **g)** UV light **[1 mark]**

AO1   **h)** Bromomethane **[1 mark]**

AO1   **2.a)** C_4H_8 **[1 mark]**

AO1   **b)** C_nH_{2n} **[1 mark]**

AO1   **c)**

$$\overset{\displaystyle H}{\underset{\displaystyle H}{>}}C=C\overset{\displaystyle H}{\underset{\displaystyle H}{<}}$$

[1 mark]

AO1   **d)** but-1-ene **[1 mark]**

AO1   **e)** Molecules that have the same molecular formula **[1 mark]** but different structures **[1 mark]**

AO1   **f)** Add bromine water **[1 mark]**. The bromine water will be decolourised / turns from orange to colourless in the presence of an alkene **[1 mark]**.

AO1   **3.a)**

$$H-\overset{\displaystyle H}{\underset{\displaystyle H}{C}}-\overset{\displaystyle H}{\underset{\displaystyle H}{C}}-O-H$$

[1 mark]

AO1   **b)** Fermentation **[1 mark]**

AO1   **c)** The yeast contains an enzyme that converts the sugar to ethanol. **[1 mark]**

AO2   **d)** A lower temperature slows down the rate of reaction **[1 mark]** and so the ethanol will be produced more slowly. A higher temperature causes the enzyme in the yeast to denature **[1 mark]** and so fermentation doesn't occur **[1 mark]**.

AO1   **e)** $C_6H_{12}O_6 \longrightarrow 2C_2H_5OH + 2CO_2$ **[1 mark]**

AO1   **f)** $C_2H_4 + H_2O \longrightarrow C_2H_5OH$ **[1 mark]**

AO1   **g)** Phosphoric acid **[1 mark]**

AO1   **h)** Temperature of approximately 300°C **[1 mark]** and pressure of approximately 60–70 atmospheres (atm) **[1 mark]**

AO2   **4. Accept any three of the following:** Fermentation: Batch process – better suited for smaller quantities; Lower cost of equipment; Slower rate of production; Lower purity / yield **[3 marks]**
Accept any three of the following: Direct reaction: Continuous process; Better for larger quantities; Needs proper manufacturing plant; Immediate production; Higher purity / yield **[3 marks]**

AO1   **5.a)** Aluminium oxide **[1 mark]**

AO1   **b)** Dehydration **[1 mark]**

Answers

Physical Chemistry

Answers to Quick Test Questions

Page 69
1. Red / Pink
2. Hydrogen / H^+
3. Magnesium nitrate
4. B
5. Copper(II) sulfate, carbon dioxide and water

Page 71
1. A precipitation reaction
2. Titration
3. $H^+(aq) + OH^-(aq) \longrightarrow H_2O(l)$
4. The point where an indicator changes colour, indicating the exact point of neutralisation

Page 73
1. B
2.

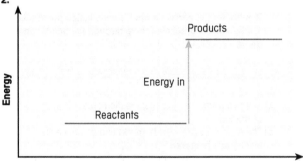

3. 2100J (50 x 4.2 x 10)
4. To ensure a fair test / enable meaningful comparisons to be made

Page 75
1. 1101kJ/mol
2. −1299kJ
3. Exothermic

Page 77
1. **Any three from:** Temperature; Concentration; Pressure (where at least one of the reactants is a gas); Surface area; Use of a catalyst
2. kinetic

Page 79
1. Powder has a greater surface area and so more collisions occur between acid particles and magnesium particles.
2. They lower the activation energy (by providing an alternative reaction pathway).

Page 81
1. A reversible reaction
2. $NH_4Cl(s) \rightleftharpoons NH_3(g) + HCl(aq)$
3. Dynamic equilibrium
4. The equilibrium moves to the right-hand side.
5. It increases (higher pressure favours the reaction that produces fewer molecules of gas).

Answers to Exam Practice Questions

AO3   **1. a)** Burette **[1 mark]**
AO1   **b)** Any alkali, e.g. sodium hydroxide **[1 mark]**
AO1   **c)** Standard solution **[1 mark]**
AO2   **d)** Any suitable indicator **[1 mark]** and correct starting **[1 mark]** and finishing colour **[1 mark]** – see table on page 68
AO1   **e)** H^+ **[1 mark]**
AO3   **f)** To ensure that concordant / consistent / reliable results were obtained. **[1 mark]**
AO1   **2. a)** copper(II) carbonate + sulfuric acid $\longrightarrow$ copper(II) sulfate + carbon dioxide + water **[1 mark]**
AO3   **b) Accept five of the following points:** Can be evidenced from diagram: Known volume of sulfuric acid; Warm; Add copper(II) carbonate; Stir; Add copper(II) carbonate until no more dissolves / no more gas is given off or fizzing seen; Filter (using filter funnel and filter paper); Heat to evaporate water / Leave in a warm place to allow water to evaporate **[5 marks]**
AO1   **c)** Any solution containing barium ions **[1 mark]** combined with any solution containing sulfate ions **[1 mark]**, e.g. barium chloride and sulfuric acid
AO3   **d)** Filter, rinse with water, dry **[1 mark]**
AO1   **e)** Precipitation **[1 mark]**
AO1   **3. a)** It is a good insulator / keeps heat in. **[1 mark]**
AO3   **b)** 14.3°C **[1 mark]**
AO1   **c)** Enthalpy change **[1 mark]**
AO1   **d)** Negative **[1 mark]**. The reaction is exothermic / products are lower in energy than the reactants **[1 mark]**
AO3   **4. a)** Points plotted correctly **[1 mark]** / smooth curve drawn as close to the points as possible **[1 mark]**
AO3   **b)** 70°C **[1 mark]**
AO1   **c)** Increased temperature increases the rate of reaction **[1 mark]**. The higher the temperature, the more kinetic energy the particles have and so the frequency of collisions / successful collisions increases. **[1 mark]**
AO1   **d)** The rate of reaction will increase **[1 mark]** because there are more acid particles per unit volume and so there will be more frequent collisions **[1 mark]**.
AO1   **5. a)** A reversible reaction **[1 mark]**
AO2   **b)** The yield of SO_3 would increase **[1 mark]**. Higher pressure favours the reaction / shifts the equilibrium **[1 mark]** to the side that produces fewer molecules of gas **[1 mark]**
AO2   **c)** The yield of SO_3 would decrease **[1 mark]**. Increasing temperature favours the endothermic reaction **[1 mark]**, which in this case is the reverse reaction **[1 mark]**.

Answers

Answers to Quick Test Questions

Page 88
1. **Any one from:** It does not corrode; It is less dense than iron.
2. **a)** Electrolysis
   b) By heating with carbon / carbon monoxide (in a blast furnace)
3. To lower the melting point, which reduces the energy costs
4. Iron ore (haematite), coke and limestone
5. Building materials and road surfaces

Page 90
1. Fractional distillation
2. It converts unwanted long-chained hydrocarbon molecules into shorter, more useful / economically beneficial molecules.
3. High temperature (600–700°C), catalyst and a high pressure
4. High temperatures, e.g. in a car engine, cause nitrogen and oxygen from the air to react with each other, forming oxides of nitrogen (NO_x gases).
5. **Any two from:** Erodes stonework; Corrodes metals; Kills aquatic life (by making rivers and lakes too acidic); Kills plants

Page 92
1. High pressure and a catalyst
2. Poly(propene)
3. **Any two from:** Plastic bags; Cling film; Detergent bottles; Packaging
4. **Any one from:** Most plastics are non-biodegradable; Wastes valuable resources; Landfill sites get filled up very quickly / they waste land
5. Condensation polymerisation

Page 95
1. **Any two from:** The manufacture of nitric acid; Fertilisers; Explosives
2. 450°C and 200 atmospheres
3. Vanadium(V) oxide
4. Hydrogen, chlorine and sodium hydroxide solution
5. $2H^+ + 2e^- \longrightarrow H_2$

Answers to Exam Practice Questions

AO1   **1. a)** Loss of oxygen / gain of electrons **[1 mark]**
AO1   **b)** Aluminium is too reactive / more reactive than carbon. **[1 mark]**

AO1   **c)** To lower the melting point **[1 mark]** in order to reduce energy costs **[1 mark]**
AO2   **d)** The oxygen formed at the anode **[1 mark]** reacts with the carbon, turning into carbon dioxide gas **[1 mark]**.
AO1   **e)** Electricity **[1 mark]**
AO2   **f)** $2O^{2-} \longrightarrow O_2 + 4e^-$ **[1 mark for each number]**
AO1   **2. a)** Kerosene **[1 mark]**
AO1   **b)** They increase. **[1 mark]**
AO1   **c)** Cracking **[1 mark]**
AO1   **d)** Silica / alumina **[1 mark]**
AO1   **3. a)** Monomers **[1 mark]**
AO1   **b)**

[1 mark for the correct atoms / bonds inside the brackets; 1 mark for the brackets (going through the bonds) and the n]

Make sure you include the bonds that connect the repeat unit at each side.

AO1   **c) Any two from:** Plastic bags; Plastic bottles; Cling film **[2 marks]**
AO1   **d)** The molecules are inert **[1 mark]** and do not easily biodegrade **[1 mark]**
AO1   **4. a)** Nitrogen – (fractional distillation) / from the air **[1 mark]**; Hydrogen – from natural gas / the cracking of hydrocarbons **[1 mark]**
AO1   **b)** Temperature of approximately 450°C **[1 mark]**, pressure of approximately 200 atmospheres **[1 mark]**, iron catalyst **[1 mark]**
AO1   **c)** To make fertilisers **[1 mark]** and nitric acid **[1 mark]**
AO1   **5. a)** Manufacture of bleach **[1 mark]**, paper **[1 mark]** and soap **[1 mark]**
AO1   **b) Any two from:** sterilising water supplies; manufacture of bleach; manufacture of hydrochloric acid; manufacture of disinfectants; manufacture of PVC **[2 marks]**
AO2   **c)** Anode: $2Cl^- \longrightarrow Cl_2 + 2e^-$ **[1 mark]**
Cathode: $2H^+ + 2e^- \longrightarrow H_2$ **[1 mark]**

Acid – a substance that produces H^+ ions in water.

Activation energy – the energy needed to break bonds to start a reaction.

Addition polymerisation – the process where many small unsaturated monomers join up to form a long carbon chain molecule (a polymer).

Addition reaction – a chemical reaction where two or more molecules join together to form a larger molecule.

Alkali – a soluble base that has a pH greater than 7.

Alkanes – a group of saturated hydrocarbons with the general formula C_nH_{2n+n}.

Alkenes – a group of unsaturated hydrocarbons with the general formula C_nH_{2n}

Anode – the positive electrode.

Atom – the smallest part of an element that can take part in a chemical reaction.

Atomic number – the number of protons in an atom.

Calorimeter – used to compare the amounts of heat energy released by the combustion of different fuels.

Catalyst – a substance that changes the rate of a chemical reaction without being used up or changed at the end of the reaction.

Cathode – the negative electrode.

Collision theory – states that for two reactant particles to react, they must collide.

Combustion – when fuels burn and release useful heat energy.

Complete combustion – when a fuel burns in a plentiful supply of oxygen.

Compound – a substance which is made up of the atoms of two (or more) elements which have been joined together in a chemical reaction.

Concentration – a measure of the amount (mass or moles) of substance dissolved in a given volume of solution.

Covalent bond – a strong bond, formed when pairs of electrons are shared; occurs between non-metal atoms.

Cracking – a process used to break up large hydrocarbon molecules into smaller, more useful molecules.

Crystallisation – a method used to separate a soluble solid from its solution when you want to collect the solid.

Diffusion – the random mixing of particles that occurs in liquids and gases.

Displacement reaction – a reaction in which a more reactive metal displaces a less reactive metal from a compound.

Distillation – a method used to separate a liquid from a mixture, in order to collect the liquid.

Dynamic equilibrium – the state in which the forward reaction is happening at the same rate as the reverse reaction. (The quantities of reactants and products stay constant.)

Electrolysis – a chemical reaction in which an ionic liquid is broken down into its elements using an electric current.

Electrolyte – a liquid or solution containing ions that is broken down during electrolysis.

Electron – a negatively charged subatomic particle that orbits the nucleus of an atom.

Electron configuration – shows how the electrons are arranged in shells around the nucleus of an atom.

Element – made up of only one kind of atom.

Empirical formula – the simplest whole number ratio of each type of atom in a compound.

Glossary of Key Words

Endothermic – a reaction in which energy is taken in.

Exothermic – a reaction in which energy is given out.

Fertiliser – any material added to the soil or applied to a plant to improve the supply of minerals and increase crop yield.

Filtration – a method used to separate an insoluble solid from a liquid.

Fractional distillation – a method used to separate mixtures of liquids; gives a better separation than simple distillation.

Gas – state of matter where molecules are very spread out.

Group – a vertical column of elements in the Periodic Table.

Haber process – a process used to make ammonia.

Halide – formed when a halogen reacts with an alkali metal.

Halogen – one of the five non-metals in Group 7 of the Periodic Table.

Hydrocarbon – an organic compound that contains only carbon and hydrogen.

Hydroxide – a negative ion consisting of one oxygen atom and one hydrogen atom (OH^-).

Incomplete combustion – when fuels burn without sufficient oxygen.

Insoluble – describes a substance that does not dissolve in a solvent (usually water).

Ion – an atom (or group of atoms) that has lost or gained electrons.

Ionic bonding – when a metal and a non-metal combine, electrons are transferred from one atom to the other, forming ions.

Ionic compound – a substance made by combining positive and negative ions, usually forming a giant ionic lattice.

Isotopes – atoms of the same elements that have the same atomic number but a different mass number.

Liquid – state of matter where particles are less spread out than in a gas but more than in a solid.

Mass number – the total number of protons and neutrons in an atom.

Mixture – a combination of two or more substances that have not reacted together chemically and are easily separated by a simple method.

Mole – a measure of the number of particles contained in a substance which contains 6×10^{23} specified particles (atoms, ions, molecules, etc).

Molecular formula – the actual whole number ratio of each type of atom in a compound.

Monomer – the individual units which join together to make a polymer.

Neutralisation – the chemical reaction that occurs when an acid and an alkali are mixed.

Neutron – a particle found in the nucleus of an atom; it has no charge and has a relative mass of 1.

Nucleus – the centre of an atom, made up of protons and neutrons.

Particle – a very small piece of matter, e.g. atom, molecule or ion.

Period – a horizontal row of elements in the Periodic Table.

Polymer – a large, long-chained molecule.

Precipitate – an insoluble solid formed during a reaction involving solutions.

Precipitation – the formation of an insoluble solid (a precipitate) when two solutions containing ions are mixed together.

Product – a substance produced in a reaction.

Proton – a positively charged particle found in the nucleus of an atom; it has a relative mass of 1.

Reactant – a starting material in a reaction.

Redox reaction – when oxidation and reduction happen at the same time.

Relative atomic mass – the mass of a particular atom compared with a twelfth of the mass of a carbon atom (the ^{12}C isotope).

Relative formula mass – the sum of the relative atomic masses of all the atoms present in the formula.

Repeat unit – part of a polymer chain whose repetition would produce the complete polymer (except for the ends).

Reversible reaction – a reaction which can take place in either direction.

Saturated – contains single bonds only.

Solid – state of matter where the particles are very close together.

Sublimation – when a substance changes from a solid to a gas without becoming a liquid.

Titration – an accurate technique that you can use to find out how much of an acid is needed to neutralise an alkali.

Unsaturated – a compound in which at least one carbon–carbon bond is a double bond.

P2 **Avogadro number** – the very large number of particles (6×10^{23}) contained in one mole of any substance (element or compound).

Contact process – the process which makes sulfuric acid.

Fermentation – a reaction which uses yeast to convert glucose into ethanol.

Yield – the amount of product made.

Notes

Notes

Periodic Table

Key

relative atomic mass
atomic symbol
name
atomic (proton) number

1	Hydrogen
1 H	hydrogen 1

1	2											3	4	5	6	7	0
																	4 **He** helium 2
7 **Li** lithium 3	9 **Be** beryllium 4											11 **B** boron 5	12 **C** carbon 6	14 **N** nitrogen 7	16 **O** oxygen 8	19 **F** fluorine 9	20 **Ne** neon 10
23 **Na** sodium 11	24 **Mg** magnesium 12											27 **Al** aluminium 13	28 **Si** silicon 14	31 **P** phosphorus 15	32 **S** sulfur 16	35.5 **Cl** chlorine 17	40 **Ar** argon 18
39 **K** potassium 19	40 **Ca** calcium 20	45 **Sc** scandium 21	48 **Ti** titanium 22	51 **V** vanadium 23	52 **Cr** chromium 24	55 **Mn** manganese 25	56 **Fe** iron 26	59 **Co** cobalt 27	59 **Ni** nickel 28	63.5 **Cu** copper 29	65 **Zn** zinc 30	70 **Ga** gallium 31	73 **Ge** germanium 32	75 **As** arsenic 33	79 **Se** selenium 34	80 **Br** bromine 35	84 **Kr** krypton 36
85 **Rb** rubidium 37	88 **Sr** strontium 38	89 **Y** yttrium 39	91 **Zr** zirconium 40	93 **Nb** niobium 41	96 **Mo** molybdenum 42	[98] **Tc** technetium 43	101 **Ru** ruthenium 44	103 **Rh** rhodium 45	106 **Pd** palladium 46	108 **Ag** silver 47	112 **Cd** cadmium 48	115 **In** indium 49	119 **Sn** tin 50	122 **Sb** antimony 51	128 **Te** tellurium 52	127 **I** iodine 53	131 **Xe** xenon 54
133 **Cs** caesium 55	137 **Ba** barium 56	139 **La*** lanthanum 57	178 **Hf** hafnium 72	181 **Ta** tantalum 73	184 **W** tungsten 74	186 **Re** rhenium 75	190 **Os** osmium 76	192 **Ir** iridium 77	195 **Pt** platinum 78	197 **Au** gold 79	201 **Hg** mercury 80	204 **Tl** thallium 81	207 **Pb** lead 82	209 **Bi** bismuth 83	[209] **Po** polonium 84	[210] **At** astatine 85	[222] **Rn** radon 86
[223] **Fr** francium 87	[226] **Ra** radium 88	[227] **Ac*** actinium 89	[261] **Rf** rutherfordium 104	[262] **Db** dubnium 105	[266] **Sg** seaborgium 106	[264] **Bh** bohrium 107	[277] **Hs** hassium 108	[268] **Mt** meitnerium 109	[271] **Ds** darmstadtium 110	[272] **Rg** roentgenium 111							

Elements with atomic numbers 112–116 have been reported but not fully authenticated

*The Lanthanoids (atomic numbers 58–71) and the Actinoids (atomic numbers 90–103) have been omitted.

Cu and **Cl** have not been rounded to the nearest whole number.

N.B. The Lanthanoids and Actinoids can also be known as Lanthanides and Actinides.

Index